THE ENEMIES
OF THE ROSE

By

G. FOX WILSON, N.D.Hort., F.R.E.S.
Entomologist to the Royal Horticultural Society

and

JOHN RAMSBOTTOM, O.B.E., Dr. Sc., M.A.
Keeper of Botany, British Museum (Natural History)

*Official Handbook produced by the Publications
Committee of the National Rose Society
of Great Britain*

BERTRAM PARK, O.B.E.
Honorary Editor

A

PREFACE

IT may be of interest to members to know that in the history of the Society this edition is the third devoted to "The Enemies of the Rose." The first was issued in 1908, the authors of which were George Massee, V.M.H., F.L.S., Principal Assistant (Cryptogams), Royal Botanic Gardens, Kew, and Fred. V. Theobald, M.A., Vice-Principal and Zoologist, South-Eastern Agricultural College, Wye, Kent.

The second was a revision of this work with many additions, which was published in 1925, Mr. Fred. V. Theobald in this instance combining with Mr. John Ramsbottom, O.B.E., Dr.Sc., M.A. There have been several re-issues.

For this, the third edition, the Council are most happy again to be able to obtain the valuable assistance of Dr. John Ramsbottom, who in conjunction with Mr. Fox Wilson, N.D.H., F.R.E.S., Entomologist at the Royal Horticultural Society's Laboratories, Wisley, Ripley, Surrey, has produced a publication which we venture to think is the most comprehensive and modern handbook yet in existence, dealing with this particular subject.

The colour plates by Miss Bunyard will help the identification of the chief insect enemies, while the coloured reproductions from photographs will be a ready means of identifying the principal diseases caused by fungi with which Roses may be attacked.   B. P.

CONTENTS.

5

COLOURED ILLUSTRATIONS.

PLATE I.—1, The Rose Chafer; 2, Cockchafer; 2a, Larva; 3, Summer Chafer; 4, Garden Chafer; 5, Leaf Weevil (*Phyllobius oblongus*), twice natural size; 6, Leaf-Cutting Bee; 6a, Damaged Leaf; 6b, Leaf-Nest; 7, Frog-hopper or Cuckoo-Spit Insect (wings expanded).

PLATE II.—1, Vapourer moth, male; 1a, Vapourer moth, female; 1b, Larva; 2, Rose Sawfly (*Emphytus*); 3, Buff Tip moth; 3a, Larva; 3b, Pupa; 4, Winter moth, male; 4a, Winter moth, female; 4b, Larva; 5, Rose Slugworm.

PLATE III.—1, Mottled Umber moth, male; 1a, Mottled Umber moth, female; 2, Tortrix moth (*Cacoecia oparana*); 3, Tortrix moth (*Notocelia aquana*); 3a, Larva; 4, Pale Tussock moth; 4a, Larva; 4b, Pupa; 5, Tortrix moth (*Pandemis heparana*); 6, Dagger moth; 6a, Larva; 7, Yellow-tail moth.

PLATE IV.—1, Feathered Thorn moth; 1a, Larva; 2, Shoulder Stripe moth; 2a, Larva; 3, Brindled Beauty moth; 3a, Larva; 4, Pale Brindled Beauty moth, male; 4a, Female; 4b, Larva.

PLATE V.—1, Rose Leaf-miner moth; 2, Lace-wing Fly; 3, Cuckoo-Spit Insect (six times enlarged); 3a, Cuckoo-Spit; 4, Leaf Tunnelled by its Larva; 4a, The Larva; 4b, The Cocoon; 5, Large Rose Aphid (*M. rosae*), Apterous female; 5a, Alate female; 5b, Cluster on Shoot; 6, Hover Fly (*Catabomba pyrastri*); 7, Lady Bird (*Adalia bipunctata*); 8, Rose Leaf-hopper; 8a, Damaged Leaf.

PLATE VI.—1, Red Spider Mite (*Tetranychus telarius*); 2, Egg; 3, Six-legged Larva (all greatly enlarged).

PLATE VII.—Mildew; *Sphaerotheca pannosa* Lév.

PLATE VIII.—Black Spot; *Actinonema Rosae* Fr.

PLATE IX.—Rust; *Phragmidium mucronatum* (Pers.) Schlecht., showing underside of leaf.

PLATE X.—Chlorosis.

9

FOREWORD

THE aim of the Rose grower, be he amateur or professional, is to have well-grown healthy plants and perfect blooms. The cultivation of the Rose from the time that God Almighty first planted a garden has brought with it the empirical knowledge of what conditions and treatments produce the best results : in later years men of science have been able to explain, at least in part, wherein lie the secrets of success and the reasons for failures.

The commercial grower, for whom Roses are a business concern and who is literally paid by results, cultivates almost by schedule. He knows the soil requirements and the most suitable temperature and humidity for his glasshouses ; moreover, he deals immediately with any outbreak of disease or pest on its appearance. The amateur in his first inexperience is liable to plant his Roses with little regard to soil or climate, to overfeed them so that they become unhealthy and prone to attack by pest and parasite, and then uses spraying apparatus which is ineffective.

In the following pages it is assumed that the accepted practices of cultivation are known and adopted, otherwise we should need to add man himself to the list of organisms which cause trouble and loss among Roses.

The title " Enemies of the Rose " was originally chosen so as to cover both fungi (and bacteria) and insects. It is customary to speak of the former as *diseases* and the latter as *pests*. Many diseases described during the past twenty years have been added to the section on fungi, and the whole brought up to date. Each author is responsible for his special section, but, as remedial measures have much in common they have, so far as possible, been generalised.

Considerable progress has been made in chemical control since the publication of the last edition. It is no longer necessary to give details of the formulae and the methods of preparation of various washes. Most insecticides and fungicides are now available as proprietary preparations under trade names, and they require only the addition of water to make them ready for application. It is important that the manufacturer's instructions be strictly followed, and materials should always be purchased from reliable firms. The lists of Approved Insecticides and Fungicides published from time to time by the Ministry of Agriculture in their Journal " Agriculture " will provide a guide to the names of such preparations.

INTRODUCTION

By G. Fox Wilson and John Ramsbottom

THE Rose grower is often disturbed by the number of pests and diseases that attack his plants, and it is possible to refer only to the more important insect and related pests which are widely distributed throughout the country, reduce considerably the beauty of the blooms and foliage, cause a serious check to growth, and lower the vigour of the plants. Reference is made to the signs of attack by pests and fungi and the cause as contributory to the effect, so that appropriate measures may be taken before irreparable damage is done.

Good cultivation is the essence of prevention, and considerable attention should be paid to maintaining health in plants by providing them with favourable conditions of soil and site. To lay too much stress upon the incidence of pests is unwise for all are readily overcome by timely applications of the right type of insecticide and fungicide so that the organism is dealt with at the stage when it is most vulnerable to attack. Early measures against such " annual " pests as Aphides (Green Flies or Plant-lice), whose rate of reproduction during their spring and summer phases is rapid, is specially desirable so that one may deal with the " ancestors " rather than with their innumerable " descendants."

Some care is necessary to avoid introducing pests on plants brought into the garden from other gardens and nurseries. Measures should be taken to avoid attacks by washing the roots clear of soil to remove any Sawfly cocoons that may be present, and to keep a watchful eye in the spring following autumnal planting for infestations of Aphides, Scale insects and caterpillars, which may arrive on the plants as eggs or as overwintering nymphs on the stems and shoots.

Constant attention so far as pests are concerned is necessary, for fresh invasions of such migratory insects as Aphides arise from neighbouring bushes, the owners of which take no measures against them. Again, several pests of cultivated plants occur also on wild Roses, and their presence in the neighbourhood of Roseries may call for special attention especially as such wild hosts are a potential danger in providing " nurseries " from which outbreaks may originate.

It is understandable that criticism is often levelled against Botanists and Zoologists with regard to scientific names of organisms, and the changes that occur in nomenclature from time to time cause confusion to many. The reason for these changes is that the Systematist must conform to the Rules of Nomenclature as laid down by International Bodies. This state of affairs cannot be overcome until a final standardization of scientific names has been achieved.

13

The Common and Scientific names of pests used throughout this edition of the Handbook follow those officially approved by the Pests and Diseases Committee of the Association of Applied Biologists (1947), and the " Check List of British Insects," by Kloet and Hinks (1945) respectively.

HEALTH AND DISEASE

In studying disease of any kind it is well to begin by considering what is health. Health, in general, means that the organs and tissues of an organism are able satisfactorily to perform their normal functions. When, however, we reduce this to its final terms we find that health in wild plants has to be regarded somewhat differently from health in cultivated plants. The criterion of health in a wild. Rose, for example, growing under natural conditions, is fitness to survive in the struggle with its complex environment, and the ability to produce viable seeds which are able to carry on the race. Do we apply this criterion to cultivated Roses ? Perfection in the horticultural sense is widely different from perfection in the wild state, just as human perfection under present day conditions is radically different from what might have been so described in neolithic times. A Rose grower sets himself ideals for his plants—and these ideals change with the years. If his plants were to be put under natural conditions is it likely that more than a

14

very small proportion of them, if any, would survive ? From this point of view we are dealing from the start with unhealthy plants, plants which by their very constitution are unable to resist the trials and struggles of unpampered existence. But a grower of Roses is not concerned with what would happen to his plants under certain theoretical conditions, except, perhaps, as he may muse as to how he might have overcome some palaeolithic monster with the hunting weapons of the period. He is dealing with plants in garden or glasshouse, and has his standards of perfection, some artificial, many natural. A cultivated Rose may be said to be healthy from the grower's point of view when it reaches these natural standards of perfection ; the other standards, such as flower colour, overgrown habit and so on, do not enter into such considerations. If it fail in these natural standards it is said to be unhealthy or diseased.

It is possible to consider disease for our present purpose as being due to (1) the innate characters of the plant ; (2) environmental conditions ; (3) parasitic organisms.

Concerning the first of these we need not delay. It is obvious to every grower that at times a plant occurs, usually a seedling, which no sort of culture appears to suit ; it is constitutionally unfit to exist.

The second is important culturally. Roses require certain treatment of the soil, certain temperature, moisture, sunlight and air in order to reach the state to which it is desired to bring them. It is important to realise that if cultural conditions are bad parasitic organisms are benefited in every way.

To understand the problems which have to be faced in dealing with parasitic disease it is necessary to have some idea of the life-histories, both of the organism attacked and the attacking organism, *i.e.*, the " host " and the " parasite." The principle is the same, no matter whether the host is man or Rose.

So far as fungi are concerned there does not appear to be any species known only on cultivated Roses, with the possible exception of the Downy Mildew (*Peronospora sparsa*). All occur on wild Roses, though fortunately not all those occurring on uncultivated forms have, so far as is known, penetrated into cultivation. It should be said, however, that considering various circumstances, cultivated Roses are remarkably free from disease ; it would be expected *a priori* that highly nurtured Roses would be more seriously affected by the natural enemies of the genus than wild species which have always been liable to attack and presumably have acquired a certain degree of immunity, even granting the fact that cultivated Roses receive special treatment.

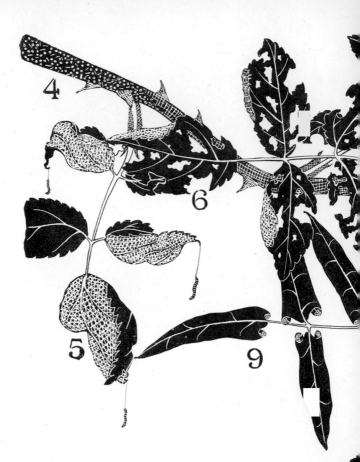

PESTS

of the

ROSE

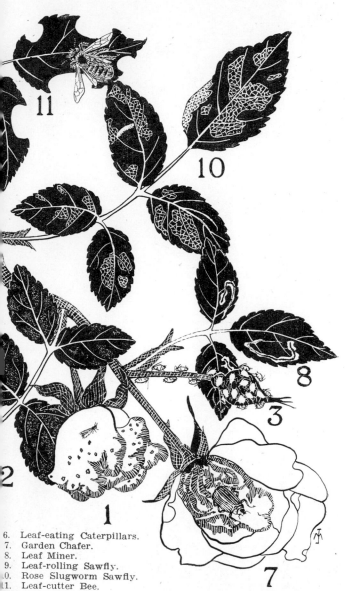

Drawn by Joyce Maynard

Part I

INSECT AND RELATED PESTS

G. Fox Wilson

The Tribe (Phylum) to which all the important Rose pests belong is the *Arthropoda* (Gr., jointed feet), and the term " insect " is often loosely applied by gardeners to any small animal that attacks his plants.

This Phylum is divided into Classes, chief of which are :—

(1) *Crustacea* (L., a shell), predominantly a class of aquatic animals, includes crabs, lobsters, prawns, shrimps, water-fleas (*Daphnia*) and Fish-lice (*Argulus*), together with Woodlice, which belong to the order *Isopoda* (Gr., equal-footed). Woodlice or Slaters are characterized by having three body divisions—head, thorax and abdomen —biting mouthparts, two pairs of antennae (feelers), and seven pairs of legs attached to the thoracic segments.

(2) *Myriapoda* (Gr., numberless footed) is divided into two Sub-Classes :—

(i) *Chilopoda* (Gr., lip-footed) or Centipedes, which have long, flattened, segmented bodies with

17

one pair of legs attached to each segment, the first pair being modified as jaw-like poison claws. These creatures are hunters, being predatory on various soil-inhabiting animals, especially Earthworms.

(ii) *Diplopoda* (Gr., double-footed) or Millepedes are elongated, worm-like animals possessing either a horny, cylindrical (*e.g.*, *Blanjulus* and *Julus*) or a broad, flattened body (*e.g.*, *Polydesmus*), with two pairs of short legs attached to most of the 60 or more body segments. They are sluggish in their habits, frequently curl up like a watch-spring when disturbed, and feed on plant tissue. They are frequently primary pests where high populations occur, such as in neglected gardens where the soil is overmoist and sour. They are also secondary pests, and are attracted to dead and decaying tissues, such as may result from an attack of other soil pests, *e.g.*, Keeled Slugs, Wireworms and Chafer grubs.

(3) *Arachnida* (Gr., a spider) include scorpions, spiders, mites, ticks and gall-mites. Spiders are predaceous and, therefore, harmless to plants. Members of the Order *Acarina* (Gr., not cut) or Mites, including the so-called Red Spider (*Plate VI*), are plant-feeders. They are distinguishable by their small size, by possessing no antennae, an oval body with no clearly defined segments, to which are attached four pairs of legs when adult and three pairs when immature. The Gall-Mites

18

(*Phytoptidae*) are microscopic in size with a worm-shaped segmented body bearing two pairs of legs attached immediately behind the head.

(4) *Insecta* (L., cut into) or *Hexapoda* (Gr., six-footed) include Insects, whose body is divided into three sections—the head, thorax and abdomen. The head bears a pair of antennae, eyes and mouthparts ; the thorax bears three pairs of legs, and usually one or two pairs of wings, though some are wingless ; while the abdomen is further segmented, and upon which are borne such appendages as cornicles (honey-tubes), cerci, forceps and, in the female, the ovipositor. Considerable structural modifications occur according to the nature of their food, the habitat in which they live, and their general habits, and they conform to a particular pattern that is most suitable to their environment.

Insects breathe differently from the higher animals and possess a series of holes (spiracles) arranged along the sides of the body through which air is taken and distributed throughout the organism in fine tubes (tracheae and tracheoles) in a manner comparable to the distribution of blood through arteries and veins in the higher animals. This specialised form of respiration is an important factor in designing insecticides to control pests with sucking mouthparts (*e.g.*, Capsid Bugs, Leaf-hoppers, Aphides, Scales and Mealy Bugs), against which Contact Washes are employed which affect either the respiratory and/or the nervous systems.

Mites (*e.g.*, Red Spiders) have no spiracles, and breathe cutaneously, that is, through the body skin.

Mouthparts of Insects

A knowledge of the type of mouthparts in insects is invaluable in knowing the most effective control methods to be applied against them. Insects and other Arthropods possess either biting (mandibulate) or piercing and/or sucking (haustellate) mouthparts. The greater number of Rose pests bite or chew their food, *e.g.*, Woodlice, Millepedes, Earwigs, the caterpillars of numerous Moths, several Beetles and Weevils together with their grubs, and Sawfly larvae. The type of mouthparts may change or remain the same during the stages through which the insect passes. For instance, Moths possess a long tubular proboscis adapted for a liquid diet of nectar, whereas their larvae (caterpillars) have biting mouthparts suitable for chewing leaves, shoots, stems, roots and boring into plant tissue (leaf-miners and tunnelling caterpillars). Such pests are directly injurious during one stage—the larval—of their life cycle. Others, for instance, Earwigs, Beetles and Weevils possess biting mouthparts both in their larval and adult stages and are, in many instances, injurious to plants in both stages.

The other group of Rose pests, which include Capsid Bugs, Leaf-hoppers, Frog-hoppers, Aphides, White Flies, Scale insects and Mealy Bugs, possess mouthparts that are modified to form organs capable of piercing the tissues of plants and extracting the sap. Among the Order *Thysanoptera* (Thrips), the imperfectly suctorial mouthparts are adapted for rasping the surface layers of leaves and shoots, while further modifications in piercing and sucking organs occur among the *Acarina* (Red Spider Mites).

Among mandibulate insects, with certain exceptions (*e.g.*, Leaf-miners, stem- and shoot-borers, and the great majority of soil pests), all leaf-devouring insects—Earwigs, caterpillars of Moths and Sawflies, Chafers and Weevils—are controlled effectively by means of a Stomach or Internal Poison (*e.g.*, DDT or Lead arsenate), which is applied as a cover wash to the foliage in a mist-like form or as a dust so that the leaf surface is covered evenly with a deposit of poisonous particles. Some soil pests, including Woodlice, Cutworms or Surface Caterpillars, and Leatherjackets, are likewise controlled with a Stomach Poison in the form of a bait consisting of an attractant (bran) and an arsenical compound (Paris Green) broadcast over the surface of the ground.

Different methods of control are necessary against sucking insects, namely, the application of a Contact Wash or Dust (Nicotine, Hexaethyl tetraphosphate, Derris, Pyrethrum, and White or Refined Petroleum emulsion), which is absorbed through the respiratory system, producing suffocation or paralysis of the nervous system.

Life Cycle of Insects

Insects undergo a series of changes or metamorphoses, which may be either incomplete or complete. Those which undergo an *incomplete* metamorphosis include Earwigs, Thrips, Capsid Bugs, Leaf- and Frog-hoppers, Aphides, White Flies, Scales and Mealy Bugs. The egg hatches into a nymph, which in most instances resembles its parents except that it is smaller, wingless and sexually immature. The nymphs undergo a series of moults, and the wings—if such are borne by the adults—develop from wing-buds on the thoracic segments. When fully fed, the nymph passes into a partial pupal stage, which is usually active, and then develops into the adult insect which is fully formed and during which stage no further external growth occurs. Such insects continue to be active and to feed from the time they hatch from their eggs into nymphs until they die as adults.

Insects with a *complete* metamorphosis include Moths, Beetles, Weevils, Flies, Sawflies, Gall-wasps, Ichneumon and related parasitic Hymenoptera, Wasps, Bees and Ants. The egg hatches into an active, feeding, growing larva, which bears little or no resemblance to the adult insect, and is termed a caterpillar, grub or maggot. Then follows a period of quiescence—the pupal or chrysalis stage—which is inactive, and during which the creature changes completely, both externally and internally, into the active, sexually mature and, generally, winged adult insect.

Such related pests as Woodlice, Millepedes, Red Spider Mites and Gall-Mites undergo little change of form during their life cycle, and their eggs give rise to creatures similar in form to their parents.

The stage during which injury is done to plants by insects varies with the species concerned. For instance, some, *e.g.*, Moths and Sawflies, are injurious *only* in the larval stages ; some, *e.g.*, the leaf-eating Phyllobius weevils, leaf-cutting Bees, and Ants as adults only ; while others, *e.g.*, Earwigs, Thrips, Capsid Bugs, Leaf-hoppers, Chafers and Otiorrhynchus weevils are injurious both in the larval or nymphal *and* adult stages.

Types of Larvae

While little confusion is liable to arise in identifying those insects whose immature stages resemble the mature (*e.g.*, Earwigs, Thrips, Capsid Bugs and Aphides), there is considerable variation, in the structure of the larvae of those that undergo a complete metamorphosis. A simple key is given to aid the grower to identify those found in the four chief Orders of insects to which belong the primary pests of Roses.

Order *Lepidoptera* (Butterflies and Moths).— The normal type of larva has a prominent head, biting mouthparts, three pairs of thoracic legs, and five pairs of abdominal feet (pro-legs, sucker-feet or claspers). Looper caterpillars of the Family *Geometridae* are similar in general appearance, but possess only two pairs of sucker-feet causing them to loop along when in motion.

Order *Coleoptera* (Beetles and Weevils).—The grubs of most beetles have a prominent head, biting mouthparts, three pairs of thoracic legs, and no abdominal feet. Those of weevils (Family *Curculionidae*) have a prominent head, biting mouthparts, and a curved, wrinkled, legless body.

Order *Diptera* (Two-winged Flies).—Two distinct types are found, namely, those (*e.g.*, Leatherjackets, Fungus Gnats and St. Mark's Fly) which have a caterpillar-like body, a defined head, biting mouthparts, and a legless body. Others, which include Hover Flies, Rose-Hip Fly, House and Stable Flies, Blue- and Greenbottles, and Anthomyid Flies, are peg-shaped with no defined head region, the jaws being reduced to a pair of mandibular hooks, and a legless, truncated body.

Order *Hymenoptera* (Sawflies).—The larvae or " false caterpillars " of these insects are readily confused with those of Moths in possessing a prominent head, biting mouthparts, three pairs of thoracic legs, but with *more* than five pairs of sucker-feet, namely, six, seven or eight pairs.

There are other characteristics, but those outlined above will allow the observer to identify the larva as belonging to one or other of the Orders mentioned.

24

Orders of Insects

Insects are classified into Orders on such characters as : (i) the presence (one or two pairs) or absence of wings ; (ii) the type of mouthparts (mandibulate or haustellate) ; (iii) metamorphosis (complete or incomplete ; and (iv) the characters of the antennae and tarsi (feelers and basal segments of the feet).

Twenty-four Orders of Insects are recognised, of which eight (marked with an asterisk) are of special importance in relation to injury in some form to Roses.

Subclass *Apterygota*

Wingless, primitive insects, with little or no metamorphosis.

Order 1—Diplura (Bristle-tails).

Order 2—Thysanura (Bristle-tails).

Order 3—Protura.

Order 4—Collembola (Springtails).

Subclass *Pterygota*

Winged insects, occasionally wingless, with marked metamorphosis.

Division I. *Exopterygota*

Insects passing through a slight metamorphosis, rarely accompanied by a pupal stage. Wings develop externally, and immature stages known as nymphs.

Order 5—Orthoptera (Cockroaches, Crickets, Grass-hoppers).

Order 6—Isoptera (Termites).

Order 7—Plecoptera (Stone-flies).

Order 8—Embioptera (Web-spinners).

Order 9—Dermaptera* (Earwigs).

Order 10—Ephemeroptera (May-flies).

Order 11—Odonata (Dragonflies).

Order 12—Psocoptera (Psocids).

Order 13—Anoplura (Biting and Sucking Lice).

Order 14—Thysanoptera* (Thrips).

Order 15—Hemiptera*.
>Heteroptera (Capsid and Plant Bugs).
>Homoptera (Leaf- and Frog-hoppers, Aphides, White Flies, Scales, Mealy Bugs).

Division II. *Endopterygota*

Insects passing through a complete metamorphosis, always accompanied by a pupal stage. Wings develop internally and the immature stages known as larvae (caterpillars, grubs or maggots).

Order 16—Neuroptera* (Lacewing-flies).

Order 17—Mecoptera (Scorpion-flies).

Order 18—Trichoptera (Caddis-flies).

Order 19—Lepidoptera* (Butterflies and Moths).

Order 20—Coleoptera* (Beetles and Weevils).

Order 21—Strepsiptera (Stylops).

Order 22—Hymenoptera* (Sawflies, Gall-wasps, Ichneumon-flies, Wasps, Bees and Ants).

Order 23—Diptera* (Flies, Gall-Midges, Rose-Hip Fly).

Order 24—Aphaniptera (Fleas).

FIG. 1.
Rose buds and blooms injured by the Rose Thrips,
Thrips fuscipennis.

ORDER THYSANOPTERA—THRIPS

Thrips, also known as Thunder- and Black-flies, are serious pests of Roses both under glass and in the open garden, especially during hot dry summers. They swarm over the foliage, shoots, flower buds and in the open blooms, producing a mottled and marbled effect on the leaves, distortion of the young tender shoots, and discoloration of the buds and flowers, particularly along the marginal areas of the petals (*Figure* 1).

The adult insects are slender, elongated, narrow-bodied, seldom exceeding $\frac{1}{10}$ inch in length, and are black or dark brown in colour. They possess two pairs of narrow wings fringed profusely with long fine hairs, bead-like antennae, and stylet-like rasping mouthparts.

The eggs are somewhat large for the size of the insect, and are inserted within the tissues of the leaves, shoots and flowers. The immature stages, known as nymphs, resemble their parents, but are smaller, wingless, vary in colour from pale yellow to reddish-yellow, and are sexually immature. They feed by lacerating and breaking up the tissues, and sucking the mashed food through their imperfectly suctorial mouthparts.

A number of species have been recorded on Roses, but some had merely alighted on the plants during their journey to their normal hosts ; another, namely, the Onion Thrips, *Thrips tabaci* Lind., while a serious pest of many glasshouse plants and occurs on several plants in the open, is not of

27

special economic importance so far as Roses are concerned ; while others, *e.g.*, the Rose Thrips, *Thrips fuscipennis* Hal., are primary pests of Roses and cause considerable damage.

T. fuscipennis overwinters under glass in crevices of the brick- and woodwork, and beneath the bark on old Rose stems. A few adults may continue to feed throughout the winter in heated houses, and may be found on the young shoots and in the blooms of forced plants. Injury to forced blooms may be severe in the early part of the season, and measures must be taken immediately to stem an attack either by timely applications of DDT, HETP, or an atomized Pyrethrum; or by routine fumigation with DDT or Nicotine vapours.

The eggs are deposited both within the tissues of the outer petals at the period when the calyx commences to open out, and in the foliage of " water shoots." The effect is malformation of the petals when the blooms develop. Similar injury may occur on outdoor plants during the summer.

The Flower Thrips, *Frankliniella intonsa* Trybom, is a dominant species in Rose gardens where it attacks the flower buds and open blooms during the summer and early autumn. It is specially abundant in hot dry spells, and was a common pest in 1947.

ORDER HEMIPTERA

This Order is divided into two Sub-Orders, namely, the *Heteroptera* and the *Homoptera*, members of which possess sucking mouthparts. The former include those insects termed Bugs, and include the Plant or Stink, Rhododendron, Capsid and Bed bugs ; together with several aquatic insects, *e.g.*, the Water-boatmen, Water-skaters and Water-scorpions. Such insects have the two pairs of wings dissimilar in structure, the first pair being modified into hemelytra ; and both pairs, when at rest, overlap and lie flat on the body.

The *Homoptera* includes a wide range of insects, namely, Leaf- and Frog-hoppers, White Flies, Suckers (Psyllids), Green-flies or Plant Lice (Aphides), Scale insects and Mealy Bugs. Their wings are similar in structure, being either membraneous or leathery and, at rest, are folded roof-like over the body.

THE COMMON GREEN CAPSID BUG

This Capsid, *Lygus pabulinus* L., has considerably widened its choice of food plants, especially in the range of its summer hosts, and is more commonly found on Roses than formerly.

The winter is passed in the egg stage—the minute, flask-shaped eggs being inserted in the shoots of fruit trees and bushes, especially Apple, Currants and Gooseberry, and in various shrubs. The eggs hatch in spring, and give rise to small, green, wingless, active nymphs that feed by inserting their needle-like stylets into the tissues and extracting the sap. The attacked leaves become

29

spotted but, as growth proceeds, the spots enlarge and holes with brownish areas appear, giving the foliage a scarred or scratched appearance (*Figure* 2). This type of injury is more pronounced on some plants, especially Currants, Gooseberry, wild and cultivated Roses, Dahlias and Potato. The nymphs when half-grown crawl away to their secondary summer hosts, which include many kinds of shrubs, annual and herbaceous plants, both cultivated and wild, and upon which they complete their life cycle. Eggs are laid upon these plants, and severe injury is done to Roses by the immature and mature Capsids during May to September. When fully developed, they return again to their primary, woody hosts upon which the winter eggs are laid.

While applications of a DDT emulsion to infested bushes during the summer are effective, the addition of Pyrethrum results in a speedier " knock-down " to these nimble and active insects. Clean cultivation is advisable, and all weeds should be destroyed by routine hoeing during June and July to eradicate all wild summer host plants in the immediate neighbourhood of cultivated Roses.

THE ROSE LEAF-HOPPER

The occurrence of pale, mottled areas on Rose leaves during the spring and summer, together with the presence of their cast- or moult-skins (" Ghost-fly ") on the underside of attacked leaves, indicates the presence of this hopper, *Typhlocyba*

FLOWER BUDS DESTROYED

Photograph B.P.

FIG. 2.

Rose foliage and flower buds injured by the Common Green
Capsid Bug, *Lygus pabulinus*.

rosae L. A severe attack results in premature leaf-fall, especially on Climbing Roses trained on walls, trellis and fences, resulting in a severe check to growth.

The active, jumping and flying, pale yellowish, adult hoppers (*Plate V*, 8) take small flying leaps into the air when the plant is disturbed. The eggs are inserted beneath the skin of the leaf, up to four being laid near together. The resultant wingless, almost colourless nymphs suck the sap, and give rise to a series of mottled or marbled areas on the upper leaf surface (*Plate V*, 8a).

All stages occur on the underside of the leaves during the summer, together with their greyish moult-skins, which are often mistaken for the insects themselves. A second brood occurs in late August and September, but less injury is done than by the first generation in May and June. The hoppers overwinter in the nymphal and pupal stages and, to a lesser degree, in the adult stage, and choose crevices between the slats of trellis-work and cracks in brickwork.

Early measures against this pest are particularly important to avoid severe leaf-mottling, premature leaf-fall and checked growth. The application of a Contact Wash, *e.g.*, Nicotine, Derris or Pyrethrum, is effective provided that the insecticide is directed to the *underside* of the leaves, thereby ensuring that the nymphal, pupal and adult stages are thoroughly wetted. The ground beneath infested plants should also be sprayed to kill those hoppers that drop to the ground during the spraying of the leaves. A Nicotine dust applied at air temperatures of 65° F. and higher will provide a more effective control than a liquid spray on wall-trained plants owing to the difficulty of wetting the lower leaf surface on dense-foliaged plants.

THE COMMON GARDEN FROG-HOPPER OR CUCKOO-SPIT INSECT

The presence of frothy or spittle-like masses on the leaves and shoots of Roses denotes the presence of the Cuckoo-spit insect (*Plate V*, 3a), which later develops into the Frog-hopper (*Plates I*, 7 ; *V*, 3).

Several species of Frog-hoppers occur in Britain, but the one associated with Roses is *Philaenus leucophthalmus* L., which attacks a number of plants, including Apple, Lavender, Geum and other herbaceous plants, as well as many weeds, especially Sorrel.

Each mass of " spittle " contains a yellowish-green, soft-bodied nymph, which feeds by sucking the sap causing the wilting of the flower buds, bending of the tender growths, and wilting of the shoots. The attack is most severe during June, and is not confined to particular kinds of Roses during severe infestations, though Climbers trained against walls and other supports appear to be more heavily attacked than bushes.

The nymphs develop into active, jumping and flying, frog-shaped insects, which vary in colour from pale yellow, through shades of brown, to

PLATE I.

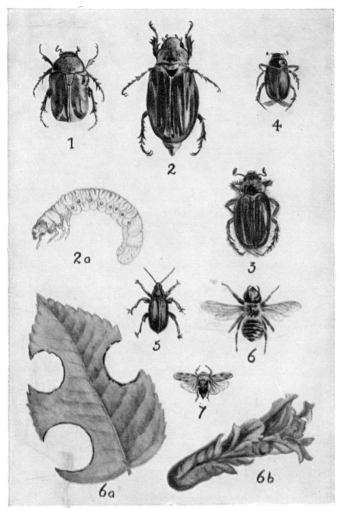

Drawn by]   *[Frances Bunyard*

1, THE ROSE CHAFER. 2, COCKCHAFER. 2a, LARVA. 3, SUMMER CHAFER. 4, GARDEN CHAFER. 5, LEAF WEEVIL (*Phyllobius oblongus*), twice natural size. 6, LEAF CUTTING BEE. 6a, DAMAGED LEAF. 6b, LEAF-NEST. 7, FROG-HOPPER OR CUCKOO-SPIT INSECT (wings expanded).

PLATE II.

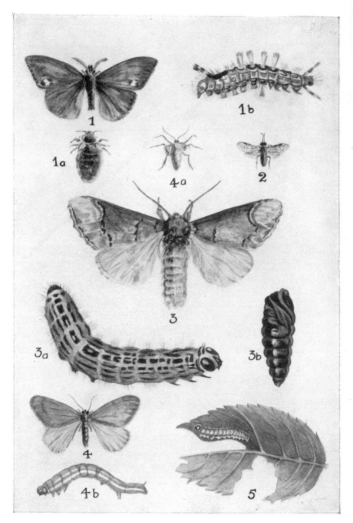

Drawn by]   [*Frances Bunyard*

1, VAPOURER MOTH, MALE. 1a. VAPOURER MOTH, FEMALE.
1b, LARVA. 2, ROSE SAWFLY (*Emphytus*). 3, BUFF TIP MOTH.
3a, LARVA. 3b, PUPA. 4, WINTER MOTH, MALE. 4a, WINTER
    MOTH, FEMALE. 4b, LARVA. 5, ROSE SLUGWORM.

PLATE III.

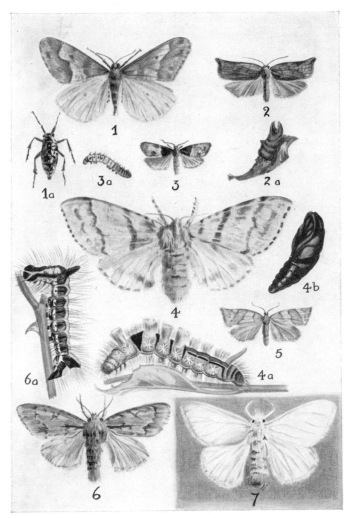

Drawn by]   *[Frances Bunyard*

1, MOTTLED UMBER MOTH, MALE. 1a, MOTTLED UMBER
MOTH, FEMALE. 2. TORTRIX MOTH (*Cacoecia oparana*). 3.
TORTRIX MOTH (*Notocelia aquana*). 3a, LARVA. 4, PALE
TUSSOCK MOTH. 4a, LARVA. 4b, PUPA. 5, TORTRIX MOTH
(*Pandemis heparana*). 6, DAGGER MOTH. 6a, LARVA. 7.
YELLOW-TAIL MOTH.

Plate IV.

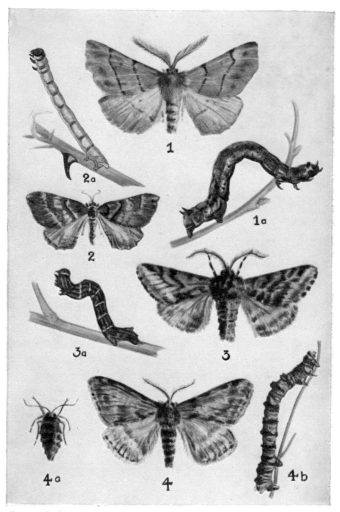

Drawn by] [Frances Bunyard

1, FEATHERED THORN MOTH. 1a, LARVA. 2, SHOULDER
STRIPE MOTH. 2a, LARVA. 3, BRINDLE BEAUTY MOTH.
3a, LARVA. 4, PALE BRINDLE BEAUTY MOTH, MALE.
4a, FEMALE. 4b, LARVA.

black. They occur on a number of plants during July to September, but do little injury to plants in the adult stage. The eggs are inserted beneath the rind and bark of a number of shrubby and climbing plants, including Virginia Creeper.

An effective control is possible only when high pressure spraying is practised so that the nymphs are wetted through their frothy surrounds. One method is to syringe the infested shoots and leaves with clear water to remove the " spittle," and then to apply a Contact Wash, *e.g.*, Nicotine, Derris or Pyrethrum. Another method is to dust the attacked plants with Nicotine dust at high air temperatures so that the vapour penetrates into the frothy surrounds of the nymphs.

GREEN FLIES OR APHIDES

A considerable number of species of Aphides are known to attack both wild and cultivated Roses, and mention is made only of those that are commonly and widely distributed.

Aphides occur chiefly on the underside of the leaves, on the young shoots and flower buds, though one species infests the roots. Some occur on Roses throughout the year, and others spend only some part of the year on the plants and migrate to a variety of other plants, both cultivated and wild.

Their rate of reproduction is very high during the spring and summer phases when parthenogenesis occurs, and females produce living young which, in a few days, produce young in a similar fashion.

33

The effect of an attack is that the vigour of the plants is reduced owing to the amount of sap extracted and to premature leaf-fall. The shoots are crippled, and the leaves malformed and disfigured by the deposition of honeydew, which is a sweet, sticky fluid excreted by the insects, and provides a medium favourable to the growth of non-parasitic fungi, known as Sooty Moulds. The presence of this soot-like deposit on the foliage and shoots is indicative not only of Aphid attacks, but also of infestations of White Flies, Scales and Mealy Bugs, and hinders the normal functions— assimilation and respiration—of the leaf.

A common fault among Rose growers is an excess of feeding whereby the plants are supplied with large amounts of nitrogenous matter (stable manure and composting material) to the exclusion of other plant nutrients. This over-feeding encourages the production of soft, sappy growths, which are favoured by sucking insects, especially Aphides.

Most species of Aphides undergo a complicated life-cycle, and migrate from their primary host plants—usually of a woody nature, e.g., shrubs and trees—to secondary summer food plants, which often belong to widely different Orders, and comprise both annual and herbaceous cultivated and wild plants. The normal life-cycle is that eggs are laid on the primary host in autumn by oviparous females, and these give rise in the following spring to the so-called " Stem Mothers," which are all females and produce living young. Each of these

34

young Aphides become mature in a short time (*Plate V*, 5) and produces other individuals, which are likewise females (*Plate V*, 5*b*). Sooner or later a winged generation of females is produced (*Plate V*, 5*a*), which fly off to the secondary, summer hosts, and there commence reproducing wingless females which themselves produce living young throughout the summer. In late summer and early autumn, winged " return migrants " arise which fly back to their primary host plants, and there produce a brood of wingless egg-laying females, winged males appearing about the same time. The egg-laying females are fertilized by the males, and eggs are produced and deposited on the stem, branches and shoots and in the bud axils as the case may be. There are many variations in the life-cycle of Aphides, but the normal type is described.

The migration from winter to summer hosts accounts for the sudden disappearance of many species of Aphides from Roses, and their often equally sudden reappearance in September and October.

The identification of Aphid species requires the technical knowledge of the systematist, and many incorrect records are due to faulty determinations made by untrained observers.

The Rose aphid, *Macrosiphum rosae* L., is the commonest species found on cultivated Roses. It overwinters on the plants in the egg stage, though some wingless forms may continue to live and breed on the plants throughout the year in sheltered positions. Some migration by winged forms to Teasles occurs in early summer as well as to other Roses, upon which they rapidly produce such large colonies on the shoots as frequently to smother them completely.

The wingless female is green or red, with long black cornicles (honey-tubes) and a yellowish-green tail. The eggs, which are laid in November and even in December, are at first a pale straw colour, but soon become shiny black.

The repeated invasions that occur throughout the spring, summer and early autumn make it essential to apply repeated applications of a Contact Wash in order to keep the pest in check.

The Rose-Grain aphid, *Metopolophium dirhodum* Walker, is an abundant species on Roses from April to November, though migrants fly off to various grasses, wheat and oats. Infestations are common in glasshouses into which the pest may be taken on Rose stocks. The general appearance is green to yellowish with the antennae and cornicles pale green.

The Small Green Rose aphid, *Pentatrichopus tetrahodus* Walker, is a much smaller species, and occurs on both wild and cultivated Roses throughout the year. Severe attacks arise from time to time, especially in the North, but it was, however, a dominant species on Roses in the Southern counties during 1945. It clusters under the leaves on the young shoots during May, and can produce severe damage, especially on Climbers. Colonies may be found on the leaves throughout mild winters, especially in sheltered positions.

The Rose and Columbine aphid, *Longicaudus trirhodus* Walker, occurs on the leaves and flower buds of Roses usually in small colonies, but appears to do comparatively little damage. It overwinters in the egg stage on Roses, and the aphides may be found on the plants until late May or early June when the winged migrants fly to Aquilegias upon which they breed rapidly, and cause considerable injury. A return migration to Roses occurs from late August to early October when sexual broods appear and eggs are laid. Great colour variation is found in this species and several varietal forms have been described.

The Rose Root aphid, *Cinara rosae* Cholod, is an introduced species from the Continent, and is now established in many parts of the country. Masses of shining black eggs, which are laid in autumn, are clearly visible on the lower portions of the stems of both bush and climbing Roses. The dark brown to near black, plump, oval-bodied, wingless females are found on the roots and underground stem of Roses during the summer and early autumn, and are attended by Ants. A close watch should be kept for the egg-masses and the wingless aphides on plants brought in from nurseries and gardens. The eggs should be removed by rubbing, and the root aphides by washing the roots clear of soil before planting.

Natural Enemies.—It is fortunate that Aphides

37

have many enemies, which aid in reducing populations, otherwise plants would be completely overwhelmed by vast hordes of these pests owing to their very rapid rate of reproduction.

Many birds, including Tits and Sparrows, search diligently the leaves and shoots for Aphides, especially for their nestlings.

Beneficial insects include : (i) predators, *e.g.*, Ladybirds (*Plate V*, 7) and their larvae, and the larvae of various Hover Flies and of Lacewing-flies (*Plate* V, 6 *and* 2) ; and (ii) parasites, *e.g.*, *Aphidius* and other Hymenopterous insects, the larvae of which live as internal parasites within the body of their host.

The species of Ladybirds found on Roses are the two-spotted, *Adalia bipunctata* L., and the seven spotted, *Coccinella septempunctata* L., together with their slate-grey, yellow-spotted, crocodile-shaped larvae or " niggers," which feed voraciously upon Aphides during the summer.

Several species of Hover Flies (*Syrphidae*) place their elongated, tessellated, white eggs among or near colonies of Aphides, and the leech-like, grey, greenish or reddish, legless larvae attack their hosts, the body juices of which they suck.

The Lacewing-flies (*Chrysopidae*) are delicate, pale green, fairy-like, netted-winged insects which lay their curious stalked eggs on the leaves. Their larvae are provided with large sickle-shaped jaws through which the body fluids of their victims are imbibed.

The term Ichneumon-fly covers a vast number

of Hymenopterous insects, including Braconid-wasps (*Aphidius*), which deposit their eggs within the body of their host, and the larvae feed as internal parasites. The dried empty skins of parasitised Aphides appear as straw-coloured, pearl-like objects adhering to the shoots and leaves. The adult, four-winged insects emerge through a minute circular hole in the region of the abdomen.

Despite these natural checks, cultivated Roses become heavily infested with Aphides owing chiefly to the late appearance in the season of their predatory and parasitic enemies. It is essential, therefore, to take direct measures against these pernicious pests, and to act early in the season before large populations are built up. It is necessary to make two or more applications of a Contact Wash or dust to control fresh invasions that arise from wild Roses, from weeds, and from neighbouring plants, the owners of which take no measures against such pests.

SCALE INSECTS OR COCCIDS

The shoots and stems of wild and cultivated Roses are frequently encrusted with scale insects, including the Scurfy, Brown and Nut Scales, especially in the case of neglected bushes.

The commonest scale on wild and cultivated plants is the Scurfy—incorrectly termed Scurvy—Scale, *Aulacaspis rosae* Bouché. It is of frequent occurrence on hedge plants, especially *RR. rugosa* and *macrocarpa*, and on Briars used as stocks.

The infested stems are encrusted with round,

flat, whitish scales—the female insects—and as many elongated, smaller, white scales—the males (*Figure* 3). The minute, adult, two-winged males appear during early summer, and pair with the wingless females—the eggs being laid beneath the scaly covering during July and early August. The orange-coloured nymphs crawl from beneath the old female scales and wander freely for a time over the plants, giving the stems the appearance of having been dusted with red pepper. The nymphs soon settle down to a sedentary existence, and feed by inserting their long piercing stylets into the tissues and sucking the sap. Their bodies gradually become covered with a scaly structure, and they become either roundish or elongated in form according to their sex.

The effect of a severe infestation is unsightly owing to the scurfy appearance of the stem and shoots, while growth is seriously checked.

The Brown or Peach Scale, *Eulecanium corni* Bouché, is a widespread pest of fruit trees and bushes (Peach, Nectarine, Currants and Gooseberry) and of ornamental trees and shrubs (Ceanothus, Cotoneaster, Escallonia, Ribes, Roses and other plants).

The white, dust-like eggs are deposited beneath the reddish-brown, oval, flat beneath and highly convex above, female scales during July. They hatch into minute, light brown, oval nymphs, which run about for a time over the plants, and settle down for the winter on the stems and shoots

FIG. 3.
Rose shoots infested with Scurfy Scale, *Aulacaspis rosae*.

and, if the host plant is evergreen, on the leaves. Large quantities of honeydew are excreted, which drips on the foliage and shoots and provides a medium favourable to the growth of non-parasitic fungi—Sooty Moulds.

A pale scar remains on the stem or shoot from which the adult female scale is detached. This pest is of common occurrence in neglected gardens on well-established wall-trained Climbing Roses, and on pot-grown glasshouse plants.

The Nut Scale, *Eulecanium coryli* L., is a closely related species with a similar life history to that of the Brown Scale. It is similar in appearance except that its form is sub-spherical and the sides of the scale often project beyond the base.

It favours wall-trained plants, especially Pyracanthas, Roses and other climbers grown in sheltered positions.

The complete eradication of these Coccids is possible by timely applications of a Contact insecticide. The vulnerable period of their life cycle is early autumn during the immature, nymphal stages. A thorough and forceful application of a White Oil and Nicotine emulsion (Summer White Oil, 1 pint ; Nicotine, 1 fl. oz. ; and Water, 10 gallons) in September, or a 3 per cent. Tar Oil wash in late December will prove effective.

Mealy Bugs, *Pseudococcus species*, are, with certain exceptions, glasshouse pests. They differ from Scale insects in possessing a white, waxy or mealy covering instead of a scaly one, in being

41

active during their immature (nymphal) and adult stages, and in having the eggs embedded in a waxy, sac-like mass or ovisac.

They feed in a manner similar to Scale insects, and breeding is continuous throughout the year under glasshouse conditions where they attack a very wide range of plants, including Camellia, Citrus, Vines and Roses.

There are several species found in glasshouses, including *Pseudococcus citri* Risso, *P. adonidum* L., and *P. maritimus* Ehrh., and others, all of which are pernicious pests and difficult to eradicate completely once they have become established. This is due to their waxy coat, which is impervious to many spray fluids, and to their habit of crawling for shelter into curled leaves, beneath old bark, leaf-sheaths and bud axils, where they are protected from the action of washes and fumigants. Control measures to be effective must be persisted with throughout the season.

Small colonies of bugs on forced Roses require dabbing with a paint brush dipped in Methylated spirit, while severely infested plants should be sprayed at intervals with a Nicotine Substitute (*e.g.*, H E T P) applied forcefully and thoroughly to ensure that all parts of the plants are well wetted by the insecticide.

ORDER—LEPIDOPTERA

Members of this Order include Butterflies and Moths, the adults of which live on a liquid diet (nectar, fruit juices, honeydew, etc.) imbibed through their tubular sucking proboscis, while the larvae (caterpillars) possess biting mouthparts and chew, with some exceptions, various parts of plants, including the roots, leaves, buds, blossoms, fruits and wood. The larvae are of two distinct types, namely, those that possess five pairs of sucker-feet or prolegs, and those—the Loopers—with only two pairs of prolegs (*see pp*. 23, 44, 45).

The injury to Roses consists of : (i) partial or complete defoliation (Buff-tip, Lackey, Vapourer and Winter Moths) ; (ii) leaf-rolling (Tortrix Moths or " Rose Maggots ") ; (iii) bud and flower injury (Tortrix Moths) ; (iv) leaf-skeletonising (Yellow-tail and Buff-tip Moths) ; and (v) leaf-mining (Rose Leaf-miner Moth).

While a large number of species of Moths have been recorded on Roses, only a few are major pests. Others occur occasionally, and generally as isolated specimens only so that little damage is done.

The following list includes the more common Rose-infesting caterpillars, the type of damage committed, and the months during which injury may be expected. It is considered unnecessary to give detailed descriptions of the adult and larval stages, for such information is readily available elsewhere. Coloured illustrations will be found of many of the more common species of Rose-infesting Moths.

Scientific Name	Common Name	Type of Damage	Months	Plate and Figure
MACROLEPIDOPTERA				
Apatele psi L.	Grey Dagger	Leaves eaten	VII-IX	III, 6, 6a
A. rumicis L.	Knot Grass	Leaves and terminal buds	VII-IX	
Dasychira pudibunda L.	Pale Tussock (Hop Dog)	Leaves eaten	VII-IX	III, 4, 4a, 4b
Euproctis chrysorrhœa L.	Yellow-tail	Leaves skeletonised (autumn)	VIII-V	III, 7
Malacosoma neustria L.	Lackey	Leaves eaten	IV-VI	
Melanchra persicariae L.	Dot	Leaves eaten	VIII-X	
Orthosia advena Schiff.	Northern Drab	Leaves eaten	IV-VI	
Orgyia antiqua L.	Vapourer	Leaves eaten	V-VIII	II, 1, 1a, 1b
Phalera bucephala L.	Buff-tip	Leaves skeletonised by young larvæ	VIII-IX	II, 3, 3a, 3b
Geometers or " Looper Caterpillars "				
Biston betularia L.	Peppered	Leaves eaten	VII-X	
Colotois pennaria L.	Feathered Thorn	Leaves eaten	IV-VI	IV, 1, 1a
Earophila badiata Schiff.	Shoulder Stripe	Leaves eaten	V-VII	IV, 2, 2a
Erannis defoliaria Clerck	Mottled Umber	Leaves and blossom buds	V-VII	III, 1, 1a

Scientific Name	Common Name	Type of Damage	Months	Plate and Figure
Lycia hirtaria Clerck	Brindle Beauty	Leaves eaten	V-VII	IV, 3, 3a
Operophtera brumata L.	Winter	Leaves and blossom buds	IV-VI	II, 4, 4a, 4b
Ourapteryx sambucaria L.	Swallow-tailed	Leaves eaten	VIII-VI	
Phigalia pilosaria Schiff.	Pale Brindled Beauty	Leaves eaten	IV-VI	IV, 4, 4a, 4b
Plusiads or " Semi-Loopers "				
Plusia gamma L.	Silver Y.	Leaves eaten	VI-IV	
MICROLEPIDOPTERA				
Tortrix Moths				
Cacoecia oparana L.	Green Rose Maggot	Leaves rolled	V-VI	III, 2, 2a
Eucosma tripunctana Fabr.	Red Rose M.	Leaves rolled and buds eaten	IV-VII	
Notocelia aquana Hübn.	Brown Rose M.	Leaves rolled and shoots eaten	V-VI	III, 3, 3a
Pandemis heparana Schiff.	Green Rose M.	Leaves rolled	V-VI	III, 5
P. cerasana Hübn.	Green Rose M.	Leaves rolled	V-VI	
Peronia holmiana L.	Yellow Rose M.	Leaves rolled	V-VI	
Tineid Moths				
Stigmella anomalella Göze	Rose Leaf-Miner	Serpentine mines in leaves	VII, IX-X	V, 1, 4, 4a, 4b

45

The above-mentioned species feed during their larval stages on the aerial portions of plants, including the leaves, buds, shoots, flower buds, open blooms and, occasionally, fruits. With the exception of the Rose Leaf-Miner, all are readily controlled either by handpicking the caterpillars where few occur, or by spraying the foliage, shoots and flower buds with a D D T emulsion with or without the addition of Pyrethrum extract. The plants should be sprayed at the first sign of attack, especially against " Rose Maggots "—the larvae of Tortrix Moths—which roll the leaves and are thus protected from the action both of contact washes and stomach poisons. Once leaf-rolling and bud-boring has commenced, the most effective control is by applying Nicotine dust at high air temperatures (65° F. and higher) when the Nicotine volatilises and the vapour penetrates into the tightly rolled leaves. Crushing the larvae within the curled leaves between finger and thumb is effective in the case of a light attack on a small number of plants.

No special measures are practicable to avoid leaf-mining attacks, but it is advisable to remove and burn infested leaves as soon as the mines are detected. This pest is more prevalent some years on both wild and cultivated Roses, but little permanent injury is done to the plants though there are some growers who consider this pest unsightly.

ORDER—COLEOPTERA

Members of this Order are known as Beetles, while those that belong to the Family *Curculionidae* are termed Weevils. Both groups possess biting mouthparts in the adult and larval stages. Beetles and Weevils are characterized by the modification of the fore-wings into hardened wing-cases or elytra that meet in a line down the back and protect, when present, the hind flight-wings. The larvae of Beetles are of diverse types, but most possess three pairs of thoracic legs and no abdominal feet.

Weevils have the head produced into a rostrum or snout, upon which are borne the elbowed antennae. Their larvae are legless, curved, and usually wrinkled.

CHAFER BEETLES

Four species of Chafers are associated with Roses, namely, (i) the Cockchafer or " May Bug," *Melolontha melolontha* L. ; (ii) Rose Chafer, *Cetonia aurata* L. ; (iii) Garden Chafer or " Bracken Clock," *Phyllopertha horticola* L. ; and, to a lesser extent, (iv) the Summer Chafer, *Amphimallon solstitialis* L.

The adult Chafers often appear in vast swarms during May and June, and attack the foliage and/or the flower buds and open blooms of Roses (*Figure* 4). The larvae, known as " White Grubs," live in the soil and feed on the roots and underground stems of a great variety of plants, both cultivated and wild.

47

While considerable damage is done to pasture and to cereal and other agricultural crops, greater injury is done in gardens where the plants attacked are mainly perennial.

(i) The Cockchafer (*Plate I*, 2) is a large beetle with a black head and thorax, reddish-brown, slightly hairy wing-cases with five raised parallel lines on each, and with the tip of the antennae clubbed.

The larva (" White Grub " or " Joe Bassett ") is a thick, fleshy, dirty-white grub with the last segments of the abdomen swollen and dark purplish-brown in colour (*Plate I*, 2a). The light brown head bears a strong pair of mandibles or jaws, with which they sever the roots and girdle the underground stems, thereby cutting off food supplies to the aerial portions. It lies in the soil in a curved position and, though sluggish when taken out of the soil, can move with ease in it, especially in light sandy ground. The fully-fed larva is about 1½ inch in length.

The Chafers fly at dusk from mid-May to early June. The eggs are laid in the ground—the females favouring dry, sandy soils for oviposition. The grubs feed on roots, tubers and underground stems of a great variety of plants. Feeding continues until the third or fourth year, depending upon climatic, soil and food factors. During cold weather, the larvae cease feeding and descend to a considerable depth in light soils. They eventually pupate in earthern cells, and the resultant Chafers

Fig. 4.

Rose blooms attacked by the Garden Chafer, *Phyllopertha horticola*.

emerge during May and June, and feed on the foliage of various trees, especially Oaks, and shrubs.

Very extensive larval damage is done to the roots and underground stems of Roses in certain districts, especially in the Home and Southern Counties, and, in particular, in the Byfleet-Weybridge areas of Surrey.

(ii) The Rose Chafer (*Plate I*, 1) is smaller than the Cockchafer, and is readily distinguished by its striking metallic, bright golden-green coloured wing-cases and thorax, the former being flecked with white spots.

The larva resembles that of the Cockchafer, but its body is clothed with rows of reddish hairs. The life history is somewhat similar, but the larvae are fully-fed within two to three years.

These handsome Chafers appear in mid-May and continue throughout June, when they are found to feed on the blooms, devouring the petals and anthers and, to some extent, the leaves. The grubs eat the young roots and partially sever the larger roots.

(iii) The Garden Chafer (*Plate I*, 4) is the smallest of the four Chafers mentioned, and varies from $\frac{1}{3}$ to $\frac{1}{2}$ inch in length. The thorax is a metallic bluish-green hue, and the wing-cases reddish-brown.

The larva resembles that of the Cockchafer, but is proportionally smaller. Unlike the last two Chafers, the adults fly in bright sunshine during June, and often appear in large swarms on lawns, golf greens and in pastures. They feed on the

49

flower buds and open blooms of Roses (*Figure* 4), on Apple and Pear fruitlets, on the young shoots of Bracken, and on the foliage of various trees and hedge plants, especially Hornbeam.

The life history is similar to that of the other Chafers, but the grubs live for one year only and attack the roots of grasses, especially lawn turf, and other plants.

(iv) The Summer Chafer (*Plate I*, 3) is larger than the Garden Chafer, being ⅔ inch in length, reddish-brown in colour and with a more hairy body.

The life history is likewise similar to that of the other Chafers, but the larvae live for two, occasionally three, years, and feed on the roots of grasses and other plants. The adults feed on Rose blooms and, in some districts, may cause considerable damage.

Particular care should be taken with the preparation of new Rose beds and borders, which are being made in freshly-broken grass and wasteland to ascertain whether there exists a high population of " White Grubs." Where severe infestations occur, the ground should be cleared of the grubs by growing annuals or a Potato crop for the first season. Great difficulty is found in dealing with an attack after the bushes have once been planted in their permanent quarters.

All grubs should be hand-picked during digging and trenching operations prior to planting and, if practicable, poultry allowed free run of the site during and following such operations.

Garden, Rose and Summer Chafers are readily destroyed on the flower buds and blooms of Roses by spraying with a D D T emulsion, to which Pyrethrum is added to speed up the toxic effect of the wash.

A dressing of Benzene hexachloride (Gammexane) to the soil of Rose beds in early June has resulted in repelling the egg-laying female Chafers.

Routine prong-hoeing of the soil of Rose beds and borders during the spring, summer and early autumn is advisable. The effect of this operation is that weeds are destroyed, the surface layers of soil are disturbed which is disliked by these pests, while some grubs are exposed to the attention of insectivorous birds, and others are killed by the mechanical action of the hoe blades.

The larvae may be killed around established plants by injecting Carbon disulphide (a Highly Inflammable liquid) into the soil. Four holes, 6-8 inches deep, are made at the cardinal points round each bush or climber, and about $\frac{1}{3}$ fl. oz. of the chemical poured in when the soil is dry. The ground should then be trodden firmly to close the holes and conserve the fumes.

The Raspberry Beetle, *Byturus tomentosus* Deg., is a well-known pest of Raspberry, Loganberry and cultivated Blackberry, and is often found in considerable numbers during early June devouring the anthers and petals of Roses. It appears to favour single blooms, and often abounds in the flowers of *Rosa Hugonis* and other species.

The life history is well-known, the female beetle laying its eggs in the blossoms of the fruits, and the larvae feed in the receptacle.

The beetles can be readily jarred off the bushes into a beating tray or old open inverted umbrella and destroyed, or the flowers may be sprayed with a Pyrethrum extract or with a Liquid Derris.

Blossom or Pollen Beetles, *Meligethes species*, are small, metallic-bluish beetles, which are chiefly important as pests of Cruciferous crops (*e.g.*, Mustard, Swede and Turnip) grown for seed. They occasionally swarm on the flowers of other plants, including Apple, Pear, Iris, Rose and Sweet Pea, and cause some injury by eating holes in the petals, devouring the anthers, and feeding on the pollen.

Control measures are similar to those advocated against the Raspberry beetle.

WEEVILS

Two distinct groups of Curculionids are associated with injury to Roses, namely, the nocturnally-active *Otiorrhynchus*, and the diurnally-active *Phyllobius* weevils.

Three species of the former genus are concerned, namely, (i) the Clay-coloured or Raspberry Weevil, *O. singularis* L. ; (ii) the Red-legged Weevil, *O. clavipes* Bonsd. ; and (iii) the Vine or Black Weevil, *O. sulcatus* Fab.—the first mentioned being the most injurious species to Roses.

(i) The Clay-coloured Weevil is $\frac{1}{4}$ inch long, and is clothed with a light brown and ashy pubescence

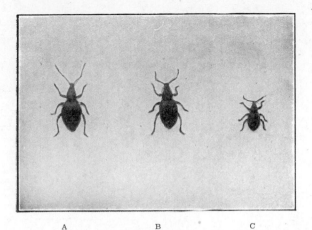

A   B   C

FIG. 5.

Weevils—A, Red-legged, *Otiorrhynchus clavipes*.
     B, Vine, *Otiorrhynchus sulcatus*.
     C, Clay-coloured, *Otiorrhynchus singularis*.

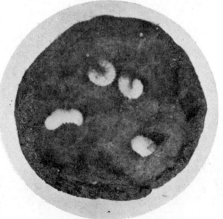

FIG. 6.
Larvae (grubs) of Vine Weevil.

and with pale yellow-brown scales that give the wing-cases a tessellated appearance (*Figure* 5 *C*).

(ii) The Red-legged Weevil is about ½ inch in length, shiny black with dull reddish legs (*Figure* 5 *A*).

(iii) The Vine Weevil resembles the last species, but is entirely black (*Figure* 5 *B*).

These weevils are wingless, and they feed at night, and shelter during the day among rubbish, in crevices in the soil, beneath stones and elsewhere.

Injury by the adult insects occurs from April to July, and consists of gnawing the stems, buds, leaves and tender shoots. The Clay-coloured Weevil gnaws the soft bark and is responsible for partially girdling the lower part of the stem and long shoots of Climbing Roses, especially those grown near hedges (*e.g.*, Yew), beneath which the weevils find shelter. The Red-legged Weevil feeds on the buds, leaves and shoots, the rind of which is gnawed off. The Vine Weevil feeds in a characteristic manner on the leaves, and removes regular notches from the marginal areas.

The creamy-white, brown-headed, legless larvae (*Figure* 6) of these weevils feed below ground from August to the following March or April on the roots, tubers, bulbs and corms of a great variety of plants both under glass (Begonia, Cyclamen and Primulas) and in the open (fruit trees, shrubs, Roses and Strawberry).

The weevils are readily trapped by placing rolled pieces of sacking or corrugated-paper, old seed boxes and boards on the ground at the base of the attacked plants. They seek the shelter of such traps during the day, and may be collected and destroyed, and the traps reset.

Injury to the basal portions of the stem of Climbers may be checked by smearing these areas with a grease-banding preparation consisting of vegetable, *not* mineral, oils.

The ground around attacked bushes and climbers should be dusted with a 5 per cent. D D T dust, which will prevent an attack by the stem-gnawing and girdling weevils. The application of a D D T emulsion to the foliage will control those species that feed on the leaves.

The other group of weevils include the Brown Leaf Weevil, *Phyllobius oblongus* L. (*Plate I*, 5), and the Silver Green Leaf Weevil, *P. argentatus* L., which are occasional pests of Roses in certain districts. These and other species of *Phyllobius* do considerable harm to fruit trees, especially young trees and Apple and Pear stocks. They appear suddenly on the trees and bushes in May and often as suddenly disappear two or three weeks later.

These weevils are active on warm, sunny days when they cluster on the young leaves and flower buds, and eat out clean-cut circular holes in the foliage and petals. Damage is seldom done to the open blooms.

The Brown Leaf Weevil is $\frac{1}{5}$ inch in length, with a black body covered with fine brown hairs, which give it the appearance of being entirely brown in colour. The Green Leaf Weevil is the same size, but is more striking owing to the shiny golden-green scales that cover the body.

The female weevils lay their eggs in the soil, and the resultant white, legless grubs feed on the roots of grasses and other plants, but are not injurious to Roses during their larval stages.

These weevils are difficult pests to control unless it is borne in mind that they swarm on the tips of the shoots and prefer to feed on the newer leaves. The application of D D T, Lead arsenate or Derris in the form of dusts or sprays are effective only provided that at least two applications are made within a week to ensure that the new growth produced after the first application is covered with the insecticide. Small outbreaks in gardens may be controlled by jarring off the weevils from the shoots and leaves on bright sunny days into a beating-tray or open inverted umbrella.

ORDER—DIPTERA

This Order includes the two-winged Flies, and is of great economic importance owing to the number of species which in their larval or adult stages are concerned with disease in man (Mosquitoes and Malaria) and warm-blooded animals (Tsetse flies and Sleeping Sickness), agricultural and horticultural crops (Hessian and Frit Flies, Fruit and Root Flies), and plants (Gall Midges and Bulb Flies). Other flies are predatory (Asilid or Robber Flies) and parasitic (Tachinid Flies) on insects, or they feed on dead and decaying organic matter, occur as scavengers in the nests of Wasps and Bees, and so on.

Only one species, however, is of concern to the Rose grower, though mention is made of two others owing to their occasional association with Roses.

The Red Bud Borer, *Thomasiniana oculiperda* Rübs., is the name given to the pink and red larvae of a Gall Midge, which live between the bud grafts and the stock of Roses and Apple. It is a sporadic pest in nurseries, but may cause severe losses among newly-budded plants.

There are three generations a year, and it is the larvae of the third brood that coincides with Rose-budding in some parts of England. The minute, female midges lay their eggs between the layers of bud-scion and stock or in any fresh slit or scratch in the stem and shoots, but never on sound stems. Several eggs are laid, and from 3-18 reddish, legless larvae feed on the sap with the result that the buds wither and die. When fully fed, they enter the soil and pupate.

Care should be taken to prevent injury to the base of the stem and shoots when cultivating the ground in Rose beds for a mechanical injury caused by the careless use of the hoe will make a wound in which the female midges may lay their eggs.

The buds and raffia for binding them should be smeared with petroleum jelly after budding. Earthing-up with soil above the level of the bud incision will tend to deter the flies from ovipositing in newly-budded Rose stocks.

The March Flies, *Bibio species*, and especially the St. Mark's Fly, *Bibio marci* L., so called on account of its appearance on the wing about St. Mark's Day (April 25th), are not primary pests of Roses. The reason for their inclusion is that numerous enquiries are received as to the nature of " pockets " of legless, caterpillar-like, slate-grey or dark brown larvae that are found among Rose roots. These larvae are saprophagous, that is, they feed on dead and decaying organic matter, and are often introduced with manure, fresh loam, leaf-mould and composting material. The concern of the grower is that they are injuring the basal portions of the stems of Rose bushes. They are, however, harmless and do not attack healthy tissues, but continue to feed on the organic matter in which they have been introduced into Rose beds and borders.

The Rose Hip Fly, *Rhagoletis alternata* Fall., attacks the fruits of Roses, both cultivated and wild. The mottled-winged flies, which belong to the Family *Trypetidae* or Fruit-flies, are seen on the plants during August when the females " sting " the fruits, causing black, pin-holed abrasions. The habit is for the flies to make many more punctures than are necessary for egg-laying. The peg-shaped, legless larvae feed in the fruits and, later, pupate as barrel-shaped puparia both in the fruits, especially in those harvested for seed, and in the ground. Thirty species of *Rosa* have been recorded as hosts in Britain, including

RR. calocarpa, canina, Moyesii, rubrifolia and *rugosa.*
While no special control measures are called for
against this pest, attention should be paid to
consignments of Rose seeds received from other
gardens and seedsmen to ascertain whether any
puparia are mixed with the seeds. The deeply-
segmented, barrel-shaped, yellowish puparia are
easily detected, and may be removed by hand or
floated off in water.

ORDER—HYMENOPTERA

This Order comprises a number of distinct types
of insects, including Sawflies, Gall-wasps, Ichneumon
and related parasitic insects, Wasps, Bees and
Ants, all of which possess two pairs of membraneous
wings, and biting or biting and lapping mouthparts.
The larval forms vary from the caterpillar-like type
of Sawflies to the fleshy, legless grubs of Gall-wasps,
Bees, Wasps and Ants.

The most injurious members of the Order so
far as Roses are concerned are Sawflies, which in
their larval stages possess three pairs of thoracic
legs and six, seven or eight pairs of prolegs (sucker
feet) without crochets or hooks, and a single ocellus
(simple eye) on each side of the head. The female
Sawflies possess an ovipositor, which acts as a saw
in cutting shallow notches or incisions in plant
tissues for placing their eggs.

SAWFLIES

About twenty species occur on Roses in this
country, some of which confine their attacks to

Roses, others are general feeders on Rosaceous plants. Mention is made only of the more common and widely distributed species of special importance.

The Large Rose Sawfly, *Arge ochropus* Gmel., is a fairly common pest of wild and cultivated Roses in the Home and Southern Counties. The eggs are laid in a double row on the shoots, each egg being deposited in a separate incision which becomes blackened. The larva is bluish-green and yellowish-black along the back, with six rows of black shining bristle-bearing tubercles. Below these, over the legs, is a large shining black spot which bears several bristles.

There are two broods a year, and larvae may be found eating the leaves from July to October. Pupation takes place in the ground beneath the attacked plants.

The Shoot-Borer Sawflies, *Ardis brunniventris* Hartig and *A. sulcata* Cameron, are true stem-borers in their larval stages, but occur only occasionally and are extremely local in their distribution.

The Leaf-Rolling Rose Sawfly, *Blennocampa pusilla* Klug, is one of the most destructive Rose-infesting species, and the damage is frequently confused with that caused by " Rose Maggots " or Tortrix leaf-rolling caterpillars. The effect of both pests is disfiguring but, while the injury by Tortricid larvae is that of a partial rolling of the leaves, damage by this Sawfly is a complete and lateral folding of the leaflets (*Figure* 7). A severe attack results in considerable loss of vigour due to the hindrance in food manufacture in the curled leaves, and to premature leaf-fall after the foliage becomes scorched in appearance.

The downward and inward rolling of the leaflets is due to the plants' reaction to a toxin injected during egg-laying, and the two sides of the leaf react to the irritant some days *before* the eggs hatch, and occurs even on those leaflets that have been " stung " by the female, but in which the eggs fail to hatch.

The black shining Sawflies, which somewhat resemble winged Queen Ants, appear in May and early June. The female, after pairing, straddles the unfolding leaflet and inserts an egg in the marginal area within the leaf tissue. The effect is that the " stung " leaflets upon opening roll downwards and inwards.

The young larva is very pale green or whitish, becoming greener with pale areas between the segments, and has conspicuous, but short, hairs along the back of the body. The head is white or brown, very shiny, with a conspicuous eye-spot.

The larvae feed on the leaf portions within the rolled foliage in which they find themselves after hatching from the eggs. Usually one larva only lives within each rolled leaflet, but it may move from one leaf to another when the food supply is exhausted. The fully-fed larva is 8-9 mm. long, and descends to the ground in July or August. It remains a few inches below ground level within

FIG. 7.

Rose leaves attacked by the Leaf-rolling
Rose Sawfly, *Blennocampa pusilla.*

Fig. 8.

Rose leaves skeletonised by the Rose
Slugworm, *Endelomyia aethiops*.

a fragile cocoon covered with soil particles and, in early spring, pupation takes place.

The adults fly actively around and above the bushes during bright sunny days in May, but they do not appear to travel far from the site from which they have emerged from their cocoons.

Both wild and cultivated Roses are attacked, and preference is shown for certain varieties of Bush and Climbing Roses. Standard Roses, though of the same variety as those grown as Bush, appear to be far less attractive to the egg-laying females. Severe attacks often occur on " suckers " where the wild Rose is used as the stock, and as such form a focal point of attack in a neglected Rosery. Certain striking varietal preferences are exhibited by this pest, and the more susceptible varieties are Betty Uprichard, Capt. Hayward, Joanna Bridge, Lady Waterlow, McGredy's Yellow and Mrs. John Laing.

The Antler Sawflies, *Cladius pectinicornis* Geoff. and *C. difformis* Panz., are pests of wild and cultivated Roses and other Rosaceous plants, including Strawberry. The larva is deep green with a yellowish tinge, and on each segment are three rows of tubercles from each of which projects a long brown hair. The body is somewhat flat and tapers towards the head and tail.

They occur on the underside of the leaves during May and June, and again in August and September, and eat irregular holes between the veins and along the marginal areas of the leaves.

The Banded Rose Sawfly, *Emphytus cinctus* L., also attacks wild and cultivated Roses. The adult Sawflies (*Plate II*, 2) appear in May and a second brood in July, when the large eggs are inserted in pocket-shaped incisions on the underside of the leaves. The larva has a light brown or yellow head, and the upper part of the body is velvety-green with greyish sides. The skin is wrinkled and beset with small, shining white tubercles. The larvae at first eat out small circular areas in the leaves without breaking through to the upper epidermis, and later commence at the edge of the leaves and eat down to the mid-rib. At rest, they remain curled up in a ball on the lower leaf surface.

When fully fed, the larvae tunnel into the pithy stems, pruning-snags, and dead shoots where they pupate. Careful inspection is required for the presence of this pest in Manetti and other stocks intended for export, and all tunnelled shoots, snags and dead wood should be cut out and burned.

The Rose Slug Sawfly, *Endelomyia aethiops* F., is equal in importance to the Leaf-rolling species for the amount of injury done to Roses. The shining black Sawflies appear on wild and cultivated Roses from mid-May to mid-June and again in July and August. The eggs are laid in the serrations at the edges of the young leaves, usually one egg being deposited within each leaf.

The larva is yellowish, but the green contents of the food canal are seen through the skin and, though a Slugworm (*Plate II*, 5), it has no coating of slime like its near relative, the Pear and Cherry black Slugworm, *Caliroa limacina* Retz.

They feed on the underside of the leaves—except in deep shade when they feed on both surfaces—and devour the entire leaf tissue, leaving only the upper epidermis unbroken. The attacked leaves have the appearance of being skeletonised and, later, dry up, turn brown, and have a scorched appearance which is papery in texture (*Figure* 8). The Slugworms occur in June and July with a second brood in August and September. When fully fed, they descend to the ground and construct cocoons in which they pupate the following spring.

General control measures against Sawflies include the application of a Stomach Poison, *e.g.*, D D T with or without Pyrethrum, against the leaf-eating species, namely, the Large Rose, Antler, Banded Rose and Rose Slug Sawflies. It is desirable to direct the wash to *both* surfaces of the leaves, especially in the case of Slugworms that tend to feed chiefly on the under epidermis.

The fact that some Sawflies may be present as larval cocoons in the soil adhering to the roots of transplanted bushes and climbers makes it advisable to wash thoroughly the roots clear of soil prior to planting in a fresh site. Bushes received from outside sources are a potential danger in this respect.

In the case of the Leaf-Rolling species, it is often sufficient to remove and burn the rolled leaves early in the season before the eggs hatch, thus

63

eradicating an infestation. An application of Nicotine dust (3-4 per cent. Nicotine) at air temperatures of 65° F. and higher will destroy many of the larvae ensconced within the tightly curled leaves, but the dust should not be applied until *after* the eggs hatch.

An effective control of adult Sawflies, especially the Leaf-Rolling *Blennocampa,* follows the application of a D D T emulsion, to which Pyrethrum has been added to provide a speedy " knock-out." A careful watch should be kept on the bushes from late April to early June for the presence of Sawflies hovering over and settling upon the foliage prior to egg-laying, and applications of either a D D T and Pyrethrum emulsion or a 5 per cent. D D T dust will provide an effective control and prevent an attack. The presence of D D T dust on the leaves has a repellent action in preventing oviposition but, as the females of some species choose the unfolded leaflets upon which to lay their eggs, two applications of the dust with an interval of 5-7 days between the dustings are necessary, thus providing a repellent cover to the leaflets that develop since the first dusting.

There is no satisfactory method of controlling the stem- and shoot-tunnelling species, namely, *Ardis,* and it is advisable to prune off and burn all dead and dying shoots, and to remove any snags which are favoured by the larvae of the Banded Rose Sawfly for pupation.

Fig. 9.

Rose shoots galled by the Bedeguar or Moss Gall-wasp,

GALL-WASPS

There are three distinct types of galls on wild Roses and, to a far lesser extent, upon cultivated plants.

The Bedeguar Gall, otherwise known as the Moss Gall, Robin's Pincushion and Sweet Briar Sponge, is due to an attack of *Rhodites rosae* L. The minute, four-winged, female "wasp" lays her eggs in the young leaf-buds of Roses in spring. The plant reacts to the stimulatory toxin injected to produce a mossy gall, which appears fresh in July and may measure from 1-4 inches in diameter (*Figure* 9). Each gall contains a number of cells, each harbouring a single, legless larva. A number of inquilines ("guests" or "cuckoos"), together with parasites on the original gall-maker and on the inquilines, may be bred from the galls in addition to the normal inhabitants.

While this gall is of common occurrence on wild Roses, it is seldom abundant on garden hybrids, though it occurs frequently on certain cultivated species, *e.g.*, *Rosa rubrifolia*.

Little deleterious effect is produced on the host plant, while their appearance is not unsightly, so that no remedial measures require to be taken against them other than cutting out and burning the galls when they appear.

The other types of galls are known as Pea Galls, being the size of a Pea seed, and occur on the underside of the leaves from July to September.

The two common species are : (i) the Smooth Pea Gall, *Rhodites eglanteriae* Hartig, which is found chiefly on Sweet Briars ; and (ii) the Spiny Pea Gall, *R. nervosus* Curtis, which has sharply pointed spines, 2-5 in number, and is less common. Each gall contains a single cell that harbours the Gall-wasp larva.

ROSE SEED FLY

The presence of perforated Rose seeds in which a minute circular hole is seen has attracted the attention of many growers whose interest lies in raising Rose species from seed. The pest concerned is *Megastigmus species*, which belongs to a Sub-Family of the *Chalcidoidea*, most members of which are parasites and hyperparasites of insects. The small Chalcid-wasps appear in summer, and lay their eggs in the developing seeds. The larvae feed within the seeds during the summer and autumn and, when fully fed, pupate within the seed. The adults emerge through a hole in the seed, and may be found on occasion along with the packeted seeds.

This pest has not yet proved sufficiently important to warrant any measures of control.

LEAF-CUTTER BEES

These wild bees somewhat resemble Hive Bees except that they are stouter and have more hairy bodies (*Plate I*, 6). There are a number of species, of which *Megachile centuncularis* L. is the commonest.

The female bees with the aid of their jaws cut out oblong and circular portions from the leaves of Roses and other plants (*Plate I*, 6*a*) to form their nests.

Some species make their nests in galleries in decaying timber (gateposts, beams and tree stumps), others in brick and stone walls, and make use of the leaf portions to form a series of thimble-shaped cells (*Plate I*, 6*b*), which are stored with a mixture of pollen and honey for the benefit of the larva that hatches from an egg laid in each cell.

The presence of a number of these bees in a Rosery results in a considerable amount of disfigurement of the foliage.

There is no effective method of controlling these Leaf-Cutters other than by capturing them in a net when they are working on the plants or by destroying their nests when they are traced.

ANTS

Several species of Ants occur in gardens, including the Common Black Ant, *Lasius niger* L., and the yellow Mound or Turf Ant, *Lasius flavus* F. They swarm over plants infested with Aphides (Green-flies), which they seek for the sweet excretion known as honeydew. Ants carry Aphides from plant to plant, which is one reason for the speedy re-infestation of sprayed bushes. They also encourage root-infesting Aphides, *e.g.*, the Rose Root aphid, *Cinara rosae* Cholod (*q.v.*).

Ants may be indirectly responsible for the death of Rose bushes owing to the upheaving of soil round the roots when making their nests and runs beneath the plants. The delicate root hairs wither owing to exposure or to being loosened from the soil particles with the result that the plants wilt and die.

They may be deterred from swarming over standard Roses by placing a narrow grease-band round the stems a foot or so above the ground, but Ants will have no reason to swarm over the plants if Aphides and other honeydew-producing insects (*e.g.*, White Fly nymphs, Scales and Mealy Bugs) infesting them are destroyed.

A completely effective method of destroying the nests is to make a hole in the centre with a dibber, and to pour into each hole about ½ fl. oz. of Carbon disulphide (a Highly Inflammable liquid), and then to tread firmly to conserve the fumes. This operation should be carried out when the soil is dry, and may be applied near to Rose bushes provided that the liquid is not poured directly on to the roots.

Some of the newer synthetic insecticides, *e.g.*, D D T and Benzene hexachloride (Gammexane) are effective in the form of dusts applied round the periphery of the nests and along the runs. Similarly, extracts of Derris and Pyrethrum may be used, but a copious watering of the nests is necessary to ensure that the insecticide penetrates into the soil and saturates the nest.

PLATE V.

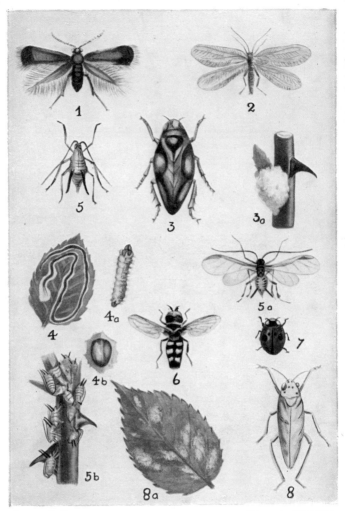

Drawn by]   [Frances Bunyard

1, ROSE LEAF-MINER MOTH. 4, LEAF TUNNELLED BY ITS
LARVA. 4a, THE LARVA. 4b, THE COCOON. 2, LACE-WING
FLY. 3, CUCKOO SPIT INSECT (6 times enlarged). 3a, CUCKOO
SPIT. 5, LARGE ROSE APHID (*M. rosae*), APTEROUS FEMALE.
5a, ALATE FEMALE. 5b, CLUSTER ON SHOOT. 6, HOVER
FLY (*Catabomba pyrastri*). 7, LADY BIRD (*Adalia bipunctata*).
8, ROSE LEAF-HOPPER. 8a, DAMAGED LEAF.

PLATE VI.

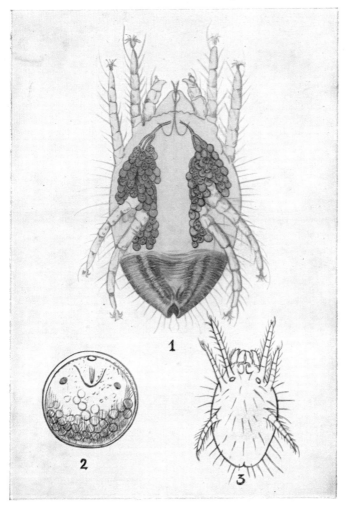

Drawn by]   [*Frances Bunyard*

1.   RED SPIDER MITE (*Tetranychus telarius*).
2.   EGG.
3.   SIX-LEGGED LARVA.
          (All greatly enlarged.)

RED SPIDER MITE

The greenhouse species, *Tetranychus telarius* L., is a pest of Roses both under glass and in the open garden, especially during hot, dry summers. It swarms on the foliage, which becomes mottled and, in severe infestations, produces chlorosis and premature leaf-fall.

This mite attacks various types of Roses, being partial to Polyanthas.

Mites can be distinguished from insects by having an unsegmented body, no antennae (feelers), and eight legs when mature (*Plate VI*, 1). They live and breed on the underside of the leaves, which become enmeshed in fine silken threads among which are seen the globular, honey-coloured eggs (*Plate VI*, 2). The newly-hatched mites are six-legged (*Plate VI*, 3) and they, together with the adults, run about among the webbing and feed by piercing the epidermis and extracting the sap.

There is considerable overlapping of generations under glasshouse conditions—breeding being continuous on forced plants from April to October. Most of the adult mites overwinter in cracks in the brick- and woodwork of the house, in support-canes, among dry rubbish and elsewhere, though a few may continue to feed throughout the winter if the temperature of the house remains above 60° F. The peak period of attack in the open garden extends from June to September, but will depend upon favourable climatic conditions.

The control of this pest in glasshouses is now possible with Azobenzene applied as a Smoke Generator or " bomb," or as an Aerosol liberated by means of an " Aerocide " gun.

The eradication of Red Spider Mite on outdoor plants will depend upon the care with which the Acaricide is applied. Effective washes include Derris, H E T P, and Lime Sulphur, though in each case the wash must be directed to the underside of the leaves to ensure that the mites are completely wetted. Forceful and thorough applications are essential, while repeated sprayings are necessary to kill those that hatch from the eggs between the sprayings. Azobenzene, on the other hand, possesses ovicidal properties, and kills the eggs as effectively as the immature and mature stages.

	Pest	*Period (in Months)* of Attack	Page
LEAVES			
Aphis-infested	Aphides	IV-IX	33
Chlorotic	Red Spider Mite	V-X	69
Defoliated,	Moth caterpillars	V-IX	44
partially or	Phyllobius Weevils	V-VI	52, 54
completely	Sawfly larvae	V-VIII	59, 61
	Leaf-Cutter Bees	VI-VIII	66
Galled	Pea-Gall Rhodites	VII-IX	65
Mined	Leaf-Miner Moth	VI-X	43, 46
Mottled	Red Spider Mite	V-X	69
	Thrips	VI-VIII	27
	Leaf-Hopper	IV-VIII	30
Rolled	Tortrix Leaf-Rollers	IV-VII	43, 45
	Leaf-Rolling Sawfly	V-VI	59, 60
Scarred	Common Green Capsid Bug	VI-VII	29
Skeletonised	Yellow-tail Moth caterpillar	VIII-IX	43, 44
	Slugworm	VI-VIII	62
FLOWERS			
Discoloured	Thrips	VI-VIII	27
Eaten	Tortrix " Rose Maggots "	V-VII	43, 45
	Chafers ; Garden, Rose and Summer	V-VI	47
	Raspberry Beetle	V-VI	51
	Pollen Beetles	V-VIII	52

71

	Pest	Period (in Months) of Attack	Page
BUDS			
Eaten	Red Bud-Borer Gall Midge	VII-IX	56
SHOOTS AND STEMS			
Aphis-infested	Aphides	IV-IX	33
Frothy Masses	Cuckoo-Spit	VI-VII	32
Galled	Rhodites Gall-wasp	VII-IX	65
Girdled	Chafer " White Grubs "	VIII-IV	47, 48
	Clay-coloured Weevil	IV-VI	52, 54
Larval Colonies	Lackey Moth caterpillars	V-VII	44
Lesions	Sawfly egg-punctures	VI-VII	58, 59
Scaly	Scurfy Scale	I-XII	39, 40
	Brown Scale	I-XII	40
	Nut Scale	I-XII	41
Tunnelled	Sawfly larvae	IX-IV	59
ROOTS			
Aphis-infested	Root Aphid	V-X	37
Eaten	Chafer " White Grubs "	VIII-IV	47, 48
	Weevil grubs	X-IV	52
FRUITS			
Punctured	Rose-Hip Fly	VIII-IX	57
SEEDS			
Eaten	Chalcid Seed-fly	IX-III	66

72

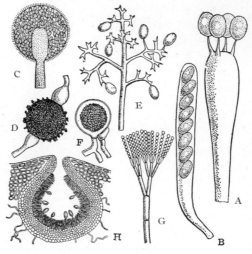

Fig. 10.

Reproduced by permission of the Trustees of the British Museum from the Author's "Handbook of the Larger British Fungi" (1923).

Spore Forms: A, Basidiomycete. B, Ascomycete. C, D, E, F, Phycomycete. C, Asexual. D, Sexual (*Zygomycete*). E, Asexual. F, Sexual (*Oomycete*). G, H, Fungi Imperfecti (G, *Hyphomycete*. H, *Sphaeropsid*).

Part II

NATURE OF FUNGI

JOHN RAMSBOTTOM, O.B.E., Dr.Sc., M.A.

To the uninitiated it always comes as a matter of surprise to learn that fungi are classed as plants. The essential character of plants to most people is the possession of the green colour which prevails in fields and woods. This green colour, which is due to what is known as *chlorophyll* (leaf-green), is absolutely necessary to plant life and thus to all life as we know it. By its aid an ordinary plant is able to build up organic food (carbohydrates) from the inorganic substances carbon-dioxide and water. Light is necessary and also a certain temperature. Fungi, like animals, not having chlorophyll, cannot make use of inorganic substances and must feed on organic materials. The ordinary diet of animals is known to everyone : that of fungi is very similar. Fungi attacking other organisms for food are known as *parasites*, those living on dead or decaying substances are called *saprophytes*.

Fungi are cryptogams ; they do not produce seeds but spores. The spores of fungi are always microscopic and are usually produced in myriads.

H

When regard is paid to the way in which weeds appear even in a well kept garden one ceases to wonder that fungus spores reach the plants they attack. When a spore germinates it puts forth a germ-tube which grows out as a thread, or *hypha*, which by further growth and branching usually forms a *mycelium*, or, as it is called in the mushroom, "spawn." It is by means of its hyphae that a parasitic fungus is able to absorb nutriment from its host plant.

CLASSIFICATION OF FUNGI

In order to understand certain facts about fungous diseases, it is necessary to have some acquaintance with the classification of fungi. Fungi are classified according to the way in which their spores arise.

BASIDIOMYCETES

Mushrooms and toadstools, fairy clubs, bracket fungi and so on have their spores borne on the outside of structures known as basidia. A *basidium* (A) almost always has four spores and is normally more or less club-shaped. The basidia are to be found on gills, on spines, lining tubes, etc., or may be enclosed within the fruit-body until maturity, as in puffballs. In certain genera, such as the Jew's Ear (*Hirneola*), the basidium has three cross walls and each of the four segments bears a spore. A similar structure results when the winter spore (*teleutospore*) of a Rust germinates and consequently the two structures are homologised and the Rust fungi (*Uredineae*) and their close relations, the Smuts (*Ustilagineae*), are usually regarded as highly specialised groups of the Basidiomycetes.

ASCOMYCETES

The cup fungi, morels, helvellas, truffles and their allies form their spores inside structures known as asci. An *ascus*, with comparatively few exceptions, contains eight spores (B). The asci may be arranged on the inner surface of cup-shaped fruit-bodies ; this is the characteristic of the group *Discomycetes*. In the other main group the asci are borne in flask-shaped structures (*perithecia*), which, when mature, open to the exterior by a pore, sometimes situated at the end of a comparatively long neck ; such fungi are classed as *Pyrenomycetes*, in certain genera of which the perithecia are buried in a hard mass of fungal tissue known as a *stroma* (*e.g., Diaporthe*). The asci may occur, usually in small numbers, in fruit-bodies which are completely closed and which must rupture for the liberation of the ascospores. This is what we find in the Erysiphaceae, to which group the common Rose Mildew (*Sphaerotheca*), belongs.

Conidial Stages and Fungi Imperfecti

In going through the following pages it will be found that certain of the diseases are caused by fungi which have two or more kinds of spores in their life-cycle. The stage which includes the basidium, or the ascus, is known as the perfect or sexual stage, as it results from some form of sexual process. It is also sometimes spoken of in Asco-mycetes as the " winter stage," because it is usually a resistant fruit-body able to carry over until the spring, when, as a rule, the ascospores germinate ; indeed, some of them will not germinate at all until after a period of rest. The mycelium of a fungus is, however, usually able to form other spores which have many special names, but for which the general term *conidium* may be used. Since conidia are usually produced in large numbers and are capable of immediate germination, they serve to extend the ravages of the fungal disease during the growing season. For this reason they are often popularly called "summer spores." Sometimes these conidia are just budded off from hyphae (*e.g.*, the *Oidium* stage of *Sphaerotheca*); at others they are borne in flask-shaped structures (*pycnidia*) resembling the perithecia of Pyreno-mycetes, except that the spores are budded off from hyphae and are not borne in asci. Such structures are seen in *Coniothyrium, Septoria*, etc. When a conidial stage is known to belong to the life-cycle of a fungus with a perfect stage it is placed with the latter, but at times we have no clue to these associations and we class the stage amongst the FUNGI IMPERFECTI—fungi in which the life-cycle is incomplete or unknown. Such forms are usually grouped into *Hyphomycetes*, where the conidia are borne free on hyphae (G), *e.g.*, *Botrytis* ; *Melan-conieae* where they occur in pustules, the wall being formed by the tissues of the host plant, *e.g.*, *Sphaceloma* ; and *Sphaeropsideae* where they arise within pycnidia (H), *e.g.*, *Coniothyrium*.

PHYCOMYCETES

A third main group contains such fungi as bread mould, salmon disease and potato disease. A compact fruit-body is never formed, but the whole fungus is filamentous, much like a green alga. Two stages are usually present, and the sexual stage, which results in a somewhat large resting spore, is formed after union of definite sexual organs. *Peronospora*, which is the only fungus we have to deal with, belongs to the *Oomycetes*, where the sexual organs are differentiated into male and female (E), and where the spores are borne on hyphae (F). The other group, *Zygomycetes*, has undifferentiated fusing segments (*gametangia*) (C) and, typically, an indefinite number of spores contained in a closed sporangium (D).

BACTERIA

Bacteria resemble fungi in having no chlorophyll ; in fact they are regarded by many as the simplest forms of fungi, though it is more convenient to treat them as a separate group. Most human disease is due to the activities of pathogenic species.

At one time it was considered that bacteria play little part in bringing about plant diseases, but during the last forty years they have been shown to be relatively important in this respect.

Bacteria are always minute, and are generally either spherical, rod-shaped or spiral. Frequently they are motile, their movements being due to flagella. The usual mode of reproduction is by direct division (fission) of the mother cell.

VIRUSES

Many diseases of plants for which no cause could be assigned are now known to be due to viruses, though the exact nature of these remains to be discovered. Sap from an infected plant, even when passed through a bacteria-proof filter-candle, is capable of inducing disease ; the virus is able to multiply. Thus it behaves as an infinitely small organism.

Since 1935 it has been shown that the viruses of several diseases are nucleo-protein crystals, so small that they measure only fractions of wave lengths of light. They have been photographed *in situ* and have been obtained pure by chemical precipitation and by centrifuging at very high speed.

Treatment

The general ideas gained from a consideration of human diseases have often given a practical man a useful standpoint from which to regard his plants. The relation between host and parasite can always be visualised as a struggle between the two. A loss of " tone " on the part of the host will always bring down the scales against it. Since childhood we have all known the adage, " Prevention is better than cure," and well-advised precautions can often be taken which prevent plant diseases to a great extent. Owing to the fact that the cells of plants are surrounded by cellulose walls, and there is consequently nothing analogous to the blood circulation of animals, we cannot apply such preventive methods as vaccination and inoculation. What steps then can be taken to prevent fungal diseases of Roses as far as possible ? As in all questions of health sanitation plays a prominent part.

Let us consider for a moment how a Rose disease spreads. Spores alight on leaves or stems of the Rose, germinate, and, most often, the tissues are permeated with its hyphae. There is at first no sign of the attack : this is an incubation period during which the fungus is absorbing nutriment. A discoloured patch is then seen on the surface, indicating that all is not well, and later the spore-bearing fruit-body of the fungus bursts the overlying tissues. Vast numbers of spores are produced, and are scattered far and wide by wind, rain, insects, clothing and so on. If they liberally infect neighbouring Roses an epidemic is the result. It is clear that the point at which to aim is the prevention of infection.

How does the first infection of spring or summer come about ? It may be that spores are transported from a neighbour's garden or from wild Roses growing in the neighbourhood, but it is more often from spores on diseased leaves or stems of the previous year. These should therefore be carefully collected or removed and burned, and not left on the plant or on the ground. A source of infection in one's own garden is naturally the most dangerous, and old Roses removed from the beds and placed in shrubberies should not be overlooked. In many diseases the mycelium of the fungus continues to live in the tissues of the wood, and the disease shows itself again the following year without re-infection. The surgical operation of cutting the diseased wood is the obvious method of eliminating the trouble, but ordinary precautions of sterilisation should be adopted in doing so ; painting with Stockholm tar is usually efficacious.

No matter how clean a garden is kept, however, it is vain to expect Roses to remain wholly free from infection. Consequently spraying with various chemicals must be resorted to. This is a prophylactic measure. It is useless to spray with the idea of killing the mycelium of a fungus entrenched within the tissues of a leaf ; such a diseased leaf remains diseased, but the portions of the fungus on the surface, particularly the spores, are killed, and infection of neighbouring leaves is prevented both in this way and from the fact that the substance deposited on the leaves acts as a poison to any spores that may alight on them. It is much the simpler matter to spray Roses before the period at which the disease usually makes its appearance. The point to be grasped is that any poisonous

PLATE VII

MILDEW

Sphaerotheca pannosa Lév.

substance is effective only so long as it remains on the plant ; if a shower of rain occurs the protection afforded by a previous spraying is immediately nullified.

From what has been said above it will be realised that the object of most spraying with fungicides is not the cure of disease, but the prevention of further infection. All the fungi causing diseases of Roses, with the exception of the common Mildew, have their mycelium buried in the tissues, and consequently protected from any solution which could harm them without at the same time seriously damaging the host plant. The principal object of spraying is to prevent the germination of the spores with their production of a germ-tube which could attack the host. The general idea underlying the application of sprays is to produce an enduring film in which a poisonous substance is gradually set free in such a way as not to affect the tender tissues of the host, and which prevents the germination of the spores.

MILDEW

(Sphaerotheca pannosa Lév. var. *Rosae* Woronichine)

Mildew is the most prevalent fungal disease of
the Rose, and is most destructive, both in the
open and under glass. In certain seasons it appears
in an epidemic form ; in no season is it entirely
absent. The first symptom is the appearance of
whitish or greyish spots on the young leaves and
shoots, which often take on a reddish or purplish
tinge. These spots spread and finally cover the
leaf as a delicate powdery layer. All the young
parts attacked are dwarfed and misshapen and
many of the injured leaves fall. In severe attacks
the tips of infected stems may be killed. Often
the young buds are affected, sometimes not opening,
and growth and flower production are seriously
interfered with. When diseased leaves are examined
under the microscope they are seen to be covered
with a network of white, slender, branched, mycelial
threads. On these threads are borne, here and
there, upright chains of spores (conidia) (A). These
are somewhat barrel-shaped and are budded off
from a basal cell. When mature the spores are
easily detached and fall from their stalks and many
lie on the leaf in masses and produce the characteristic powdery appearance. The mycelium is
attached to the leaf at various points by means of
minute suckers or *haustoria*, which penetrate the
cuticle by a narrow neck and enlarge within the

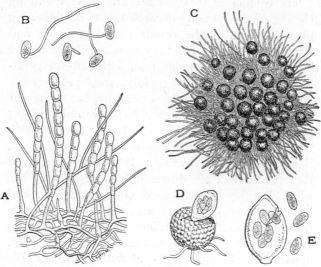

FIG. 11.

Sphaerotheca pannosa Lév. : A, Conidiophores with chains of conidia (*Oidium*). B, Germinating conidia. C, Perithecia. D, Perithecium with ascus. E, Ascus with eight ascospores.

Magnification, A, B, D, 180; C, 50; E, 240.

epidermal cells, from which they are able to absorb nutriment. Sometimes two or more haustoria are present in an epidermal cell, completely filling it. The killing of the cells may produce a darkish spot on the leaf somewhat resembling Black Spot.

The conidia as they mature are blown about by the slightest wind and are carried on to neighbouring plants, where, if the conditions of moisture and temperature be suitable, they germinate immediately by sending out, near one end, a thread-like germ-tube (B), which grows rapidly, soon producing a haustorium from which tender hyphae grow out and in a few days produce a fresh crop of conidia : germination is poor when the leaves are wet with rain or dew, and so the disease, unlike Black Spot, is less severe in wet weather. It should be remarked that the conidia are disseminated not only by the wind, but by various gardening operations, and by insects and even by snails. The conidial stage (formerly known as *Oidium leucoconium* Desm.) continues throughout the summer and early autumn, apparently being most abundant when the atmosphere is humid. However, in *Sphaerotheca* there are two kinds of spores, corresponding to an asexual stage and a sexual stage. The conidia are short-lived, retaining their vitality only for a few days, and it is to the sexual spores that the fungus owes its power of carrying on from one season to another.

Usually late in the summer the mycelium on the stem and thorns forms a dense satiny mass, shining white at first, but usually changing to a grey or buff colour. The hyphae, under the microscope, are different in appearance from the ordinary vegetative hyphae on the leaf, being densely woven, thick-walled and, at maturity, looking somewhat like glass rods. Moreover, these special hyphae are persistent and remain on the stem throughout the winter, and buried in them occur the perithecia, the perfect or sexual stage of the fungus (C). These are more or less spherical and have a hard resistant wall. Within is an ascus containing eight ascospores which mature slowly (D). In the spring the ascospores are liberated by the rupture of the wall of the fruit-body and of the ascus (E), and are able to infect any Rose leaf or young stem on which they may happen to alight. The perithecia are almost entirely confined to the stem and spines, but occasionally occur on the petioles, the mid-ribs of the leaves, the calyx, or the fruit. It is to the asexual spores or conidia (summer spores) that the fungus owes its rapid spread throughout the growing season : the sexual spores or ascospores (winter spores) enable it to withstand the inclement conditions of winter.

Owing to the fact that in gardens the sexual stage is rarely seen, an overwintering mycelium has frequently been postulated : it has been suggested that the mycelium persists in the leaf-buds where it is protected by the scales. There is, however, no convincing evidence for this. Another suggestion is that there may be chlamydospores, thick-walled resistant spores, formed within the mycelium. Under glass the temperature is probably always sufficiently high to permit of the vegetative mycelium continuing throughout the year.

There is a great difference in the susceptibility of various Roses ranging from comparative immunity in some of the glossy-leaved Wichuraiana Hybrids to great susceptibility in soft-leaved forms such as Crimson Rambler and other quickly maturing varieties. Proper aeration of plants in glass houses tends to reduce attack.

Powdery Mildew of Roses is cosmopolitan, being known wherever Roses are grown—from the Arctic Circle to the Equator.

It was formerly considered that the Mildew on peaches is the same fungus as the common Mildew on Roses, but it has been found that the conidia from one host will not infect the other : as there are also morphological differences, the fungi on the two hosts have been distinguished by varietal names.

A study of the life-cycle of the parasite suggests the following lines along which it may be attacked :—

1. To prevent the appearance of, or to destroy, the ascospore stage and thus the possibility of the spring reappearance from that source.

2. To destroy the conidial stage at its first appearance and thus prevent the production of new centres of infection. It is obvious that the two are closely connected.

The resistant perfect stage is very difficult to attack. The usual method by which such forms are dealt with is either wholly to remove them or to spray as the spores are being liberated. Infected branches may be cut out and burned, or, as the fungus is entirely superficial and is in no way immersed in the tissues, it may be scraped off. The proper time to do this is in late summer or autumn before the fruits rupture and liberate their spores. No matter with what care this is done, however, one cannot hope to keep Roses free from Mildew. Conidia of the fungus are produced in enormous numbers* and can be carried quite long distances by the wind—probably a few miles. The fungus is common on wild Roses, and in many parts of the country (in Surrey for example) the winter stage is fairly frequent on the stems.

Infection having once begun sufficient spores are formed in a few days to spread the disease to all the neighbouring plants : even a rain splash is sufficient to disperse the spores. To prevent this various fungicides are used. The mycelium of *Sphaerotheca* and the other true Mildews differs from that of almost all other diseases in being external and not buried within the tissues of the leaves. Owing to this fact sprays have a direct effect on the fungus mycelium though their chief use is not fungicidal but preventive.

---

* A calculation from A of Fig. 11 shows that there would be roughly 3,000,000 conidia in a patch an inch square.

Old infected leaves, which may bear perithecia, should be collected in autumn and burned.

The fungus is not very resistant to fungicides, though the felted mass of mycelium is difficult to wet. Many fungicides, unfortunately, discolour the leaves (*e.g.*, Bordeaux mixture, especially in wet weather) and their use is therefore not advisable.

Immediately after spring-pruning the plants should be sprayed with lime sulphur ($\frac{1}{2}$ a pint in $2\frac{1}{2}$ gallons of water), or liver of sulphur (potassium sulphide) (1 ounce in $2\frac{1}{2}$ gallons of water), or colloidal cuprous oxychloride in a white oil emulsion. When the leaves are expanded, dusting with sulphur or spraying with colloidal sulphur, two or three times at short intervals, will also control the disease. Sulphur should not be used in very hot dry summer weather as it is then liable to scorch the leaves. Under glass the addition of wetting agents to spray solutions usually increases their effectiveness. Heating pipes are often painted with a paste of sulphur and lime, but if they become too hot damage may result to the foliage from the volatilised sulphur.

PLATE VIII.

BLACK SPOT

Actinonema rosae Fr.

BLACK SPOT

(*Actinonema Rosae* Fr., *Diplocarpon Rosae* Wolf)

This disease of the Rose is second in its incidence only to Mildew, and causes far more damage. The time at which it appears is very variable, but it is usually noticeable about mid-summer and lasts until the coming of frosts. It is particularly abundant in cool damp seasons. Leaves which are more or less fully grown are those most frequently attacked and show black or purplish areas on their upper surface. Some leaves never have more than infected patches, but others are soon completely invaded and are shed much earlier than healthy ones. The leaves of some varieties of Rose fall very soon after infection, and this has been known to begin as early as June.

After defoliation a large crop of fresh leaves is usually formed at the end of the branches, from the buds which should remain dormant until the following season, with the result that the plant is weakened. These new leaves most frequently become attacked by Mildew at a very early stage.

The spots caused by *Actinonema* begin as minute black specks which enlarge until, normally, they are rounded with a very irregular fringed border and with radiating fibrils over their surface. They are usually about a quarter of an inch in diameter, but sometimes extend over the whole of the leaflet. After a time numerous minute, shining, black dots appear over the surface of the spots, concentrically arranged. These are the fructifications (B) of the fungus, which consist of masses* of spores produced from a mat of mycelium just below the cuticle of the leaf, which is first raised into a dome and is then ruptured, giving the spores access to the exterior. The spores of the fungus are hyaline or slightly greenish, two-celled, slightly curved, somewhat constricted at the septum and contain numerous oil-drops.

The spore on germination gives rise to a colourless mycelium which penetrates the cuticle of the leaf. For the most part the mycelium is localised in the epidermal cells where it has entered, but it advances both laterally and vertically in young leaves, often reaching the spongy parenchyma. The mycelium changes from hyaline to yellow and then to brown as it ages. The fructifications are always formed just within the cuticle (*i.e.*, the outermost portions of the wall) of the epidermal cells. The mycelial filaments here show a tendency to join together laterally, forming strands. It is these strands which give rise to the appearance of radiating fibrils on the surface of the spots. Generally the fructification is formed from a single strand, principally by lateral extension (A). The colour of this mycelium darkens and gradually the darkening extends to the vegetative portions. Spore formation begins about a fortnight after infection.

---

* 30,000 spores were calculated as the number produced in a single spot ; kept moist the spot was estimated to produce 2,000,000 spores in eight days.

Transverse sections of the young fructifications show the surface of the mycelial plate or stroma to have a number of short, hyaline, conical columns arising from its surface. By their growth the cuticle is raised in a dome-like manner. The columns round off at their ends, become wider, and a wall appears across their middle, thus forming a spore. The columns (*sporophores*) soon take on the general tint of the stromatic layer. The spores then become uniseptate, and may be seen oozing out in spring and early summer.

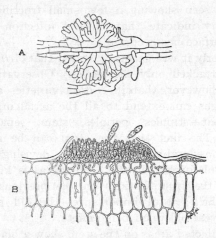

Actinonema Rosae Fr.: A, Mycelium strand within cuticle developing into spore-bed, surface view. B, Section of mature fruit-body.
Magnification, A, 400; B, 325.

In addition to the subcuticular mycelium there is an extension of mycelium into the mesophyll of the leaf, and the two masses are connected by hyphae, which pass either through the epidermal cells themselves or through their walls. It is this second type of mycelium which apparently absorbs nutriment from the leaf. The dark colour of the spots is not due to the mycelium of the fungus, but to the presence in the outer portion of the epidermis of a brown substance, which is a product of degeneration of the cell contents. Occasionally directly below a spot a small brown discoloration may be seen showing a few small fructifications. This may indicate that natural infection of the lower surface has occurred.

Formerly it was generally stated that *Actinonema Rosae* attacked only the leaves. Observation has shown, however, that in certain varieties at least the fungus can extend to all the aerial organs of the plant—stipules, petioles, stem, sepals and petals. The fact that the stem can be affected is of considerable importance in devising means of control for the disease. So far as is known it is only the fructifications on the previous year's wood which are of importance—the old pustules on two-year-old wood being effete.

The infected areas on the stem show a blackened, blistered appearance dotted with the fructifications. The mycelium is colourless and it develops entirely in the cortex, where it kills the tissue. Sometimes cavities are developed deep in the cortical tissue by the activity of the mycelium, and spores are produced in profusion and liberated into the cavities.

The perfect stage of the fungus has been recorded from America under the name *Diplocarpon Rosae* Wolf, but has not yet been found in Europe. This occurs on the fallen leaves previously attacked by the conidial stage and ripens its asci in early spring. The fruit-body is a shield-shaped structure, the upper part rupturing at maturity to liberate the spores. The systematic position of the perfect stage is somewhat doubtful : it is a Discomycete (Dermateaceae), with hyaline ellipsoid spores slightly constricted at the septum. Spermogonia have also been described as developing on old leaves in spring.

Leaves infected by Black Spot may be invaded by *Coniothyrium Fuckelii*, which is normally restricted to stems where it produces Stem Canker.

All infected leaves should be removed from the plant and from the ground and infected stems should be cut out and burned. After spring-pruning the plants should be sprayed with one of the colloidal copper sprays ; this should be repeated at weekly intervals as long as necessary.

RUST

(Phragmidium mucronatum (Pers.) Schlecht.)

This disease is very troublesome in some districts, particularly where there are early and heavy formations of dew. No variety of the cultivated Rose appears to be immune, and hardy Hybrid varieties seem particularly susceptible. Badly infected plants often die in the first year of infection.

The name " Rust " was first applied to a disease of cereals caused by a fungus closely allied to *Phragmidium.* The first stage of the disease of Roses has the same characteristic rusty colour as that of wheat rust. It is commonly known that the rust of wheat has three stages in its life-cycle, one of which occurs on the common barberry. The Rose Rust has the same stages in its development, but all occur on the Rose—there is no alternate host.

Pustules *(caeomata)* may also be produced on petioles, sepals, and even on the hips. Much more important is that they are often formed on stems. Here they arise from a mycelium which may remain alive for some years producing a steady and annual crop of aecidiospores. The patches of Rust are generally larger than on the leaf and more irregular in shape, frequently being an inch or more in length, causing distortion and curving and often destroying the buds. In winter the spore-producing layer is covered with bark. When the Rust disappears from the cracks, gaping

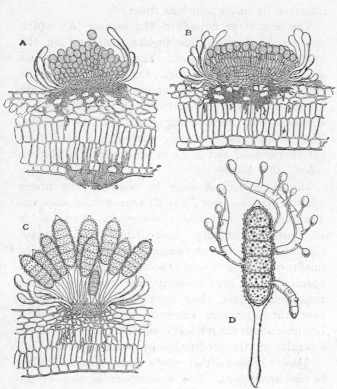

Fig. 12.

Phragmidium mucronatum (Pers.) Schlecht.: A, Section of caeoma showing aecidiospores in chains and spermogonium (s.). B, Section of uredosorus. C, Section of teleutosorus. D, Teleutospore germinating with production of septate promycelia and sporidia.

Magnification, 150.

wounds are left which are potential centres of infection by other injurious fungi.

The first stage noticed is the *caeoma* (A), which appears as a small pustule-like structure on the under surface of the leaf. The usual time for its appearance is early spring. On the rupture of the epidermis of the leaf the spores (*aecidiospores*) are liberated. These are formed in closely packed columns with intervening collapsed sterile cells. They are globose, minutely warted, and when they germinate send out a germ-tube which is able to infect other leaves.

Minute structures may be seen on the upper surface of the leaf accompanying the caeoma. These are the so-called *spermogonia* (A.s.), which are usually broadly flask-shaped and contain minute spores, the *spermatia*. There was formerly much discussion about the possible function of spermatia. It was thought that they were effete male cells, hence their name. It is now known that their present function is concerned with bringing about the nuclear condition of the mycelium essential for the production of aecidiospores.

About June another spore form appears. This is the *uredospore*. The uredospore is also bright orange coloured and differs in external appearance from the aecidiospore only by being slightly echinulate and in having numerous germ-pores. The spore bed (*sorus*) contains the stalked spores; these are borne singly, not in chains (B). They germinate by putting out a germ-tube which is

PLATE IX.

RUST

Phragmidium mucronatum (Pers.) Schlecht.
Showing underside of leaf.

able to infect new areas. The mycelium is strictly localised. Both aecidiospore and uredospore are able to germinate immediately and rapidly propagate the parasite. It should be remarked, however, that it is now held that the uredospore is the main source of new infection.

About August a change of colour occurs in the uredosorus. Formerly a bright orange, it now becomes blackish. This is due to the fact that in place of the globose brightly coloured uredospores the underlying mycelium now produces much larger, elongated, oval bodies with thickened spore wall and generally from five to eight cross walls (C). These are *teleutospores*, resting spores which are able to withstand the inclement conditions of winter and carry over the fungus to another growing season ; indeed they seem to require freezing before they will germinate. They do not germinate immediately, germination taking place the following spring.

The germination of the teleutospore is different from that of the other spores (D). Each of the separate portions of the spore is able to put forth a " germ-tube " which becomes septate, each segment then producing a spore (*sporidium*). It is this production of a promycelium or basidium that shows the close relation of Rust fungi with the Basidiomycetes, particularly with forms like the Jew's Ear. The sporidia are capable of spreading infection. The mycelium they produce gives rise to caeomata.

The life-cycle of the fungus may be represented thus : aecidiospore — uredospore — teleutospore — sporidia—aecidiospore.

There is considerable difference in the susceptibility of different varieties and stocks towards Rust. *Phragmidium mucronatum* occurs on our native *Rosa canina* and *R. spinosissima,* and is recorded on several other species, but does not spread from them to the cultivated Rose. Moreover the Rust from cultivated Roses does not attack *Rosa laxa* and certain varieties of *R. canina.* It is certain that there are specialised strains or races which are restricted in their parasitism. This is doubtless a factor which is concerned in the differences in the susceptibility of cultivated Roses, for these are in nowise homogeneous and may contain immune species in their ancestry.

Phragmidium is restricted to Rosaceae, and many different species occur on *Rosa,* particularly in America, where apparently *P. mucronatum* does not occur naturally, but has been introduced with cultivated Roses, as also in Australia.

Phragmidium subcorticium Wint.* [*P. subcorticatum* (a *lapsus calami*)] and *P. disciflorum* James are other names for the fungus.

The two sources of infection in spring are the teleutospores, which overwintered on leaves, and the aecidiospores, which are formed from the perennial

---

* This name was used in the last edition as was then customary. In 1913 I had shown that *P. mucronatum* was the valid name and this is now generally adopted.

mycelium in the stem. All infected leaves should be collected in autumn, both from the plant and from the ground, and burned, and all cankered stems should be cut out as soon as they are noticed.

Where the disease is troublesome the plants should be sprayed with copper sulphate solution or Bordeaux mixture while the buds are still dormant. After the appearance of the leaves colloidal cuprous oxide or other copper solution which does not disfigure the leaves should be used : colloidal sulphur is sometimes satisfactory. It is essential that this should reach the fungus on the *under* side of the leaf. Sulphur is not compatible with any oil spray, so that if a colloidal cuprous oxychloride white oil emulsion spray has been used for either Mildew or Black Spot, then the same spray may be used as treatment for Rust.

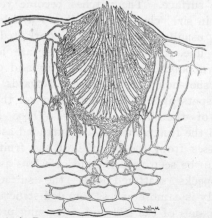

Septoria Rosae Desm.: Section of pycnidium.
Magnification, 300.

[*See page following.*

LEAF SCORCH

(*Septoria Rosae* Desm.)

The disease caused by *Septoria Rosae* is not very common in an epidemic form, though the fungus is not rare on old leaves in spots which have been previously attacked by Rust. At times, however, it causes serious damage, more especially to nursery stock. In an epidemic form the disease results in premature defoliation, affected plants being often quite leafless by the end of July. In a favourable season a second crop of leaves is produced with the usual consequent ill-effects. Roses attacked two seasons in succession rarely recover.

The disease is confined to the leaves and first appears as minute yellowish green patches scattered over the surface. The patches become yellowish, increase in size, change gradually to a pale brown and are usually bordered by a dark reddish or purplish line. When young leaves are attacked the brown patches generally fall out and give the leaf a " shot-hole " appearance. Towards autumn whitish spots appear here and there on the upper surface of the brown patches. These are the spores of the fungus, which are extruded as tendril-like masses from the mouths of the fruit-bodies, which can be seen with the aid of a lens as minute black specks scattered over the surface. The fruit-body is a more or less rounded structure sunk in the tissues of the leaf and occupying practically

FIG. 13.

Anthracnose (*Sphaceloma Rosarum* Jenkins)
The spots are sometimes confused with Black Spot.

its whole thickness. It has no strongly marked wall. From the inner part of the hyphal weft which encloses it, narrow conidiophores arise which bear numerous thread-like, septate conidia, somewhat narrower at the ends ; these fill the cavity of the structure. The spores hang together for a time after they are extruded from the short neck of the fruit which just penetrates the leaf epidermis. These spore masses break up on drying and are scattered by wind and other agencies. Alighting on a leaf they are able to cause infection.

In addition to the above pycnidial stage a perfect or ascospore stage has been described from the Continent. It is a Pyrenomycete and has been given the name *Sphaerulina Rehmiana* Jaap. It shows as groups of black dots usually on the upper surface of the leaf. These dots are the short stout necks of sunken spherical perithecia which have thick walls and contain numerous asci with eight colourless, thread-like, mostly three-septate spores. This form enables the fungus to survive the rigours of winter. The ascospores ripen in spring and bring about infection of young Rose leaves.

Septoria Rosae-arvenis Sacc. and *Septoria Rosarum* Westend. appear to be forms of the fungus discussed above.

All diseased leaves, whether on the ground or remaining on the plant, should be gathered and burned. In the spring, as the leaves open, spraying with colloidal cuprous oxide or oxychloride is reputed to be efficacious.

ANTHRACNOSE

(*Sphaceloma Rosarum* (Passer.) Jenkins)
(See Fig. 13.)

Rose Anthracnose* is not uncommon in this country, affecting both wild and cultivated plants. It is characterised by small circular spots, which appear on the upper surface of the leaves, and, less frequently, on blooms, sepals, hips and stems.

On the leaves the disease first shows as paler spots which, as they increase in size, become dark brown and then dark purplish black often with a dull brown or purplish rim. Later the centre becomes whitish or greyish owing to the lifting of the cuticle by the developing fruit-bodies. The spots are of various sizes, but usually do not exceed a quarter of an inch in diameter. They are often numerous and may occur on both surfaces of the leaflets or on any part of them.

The lesions may fall away beneath leaving only a papery upper layer, which ruptures easily, or may break apart completely, producing a " shot-hole " effect. Diseased leaflets sometimes become distorted and ragged at the margin.

---

* The term " anthracnose " was first applied to the disease of the grape caused by *Sphaceloma ampelinum* de Bary—*Gloeosporium ampelophagum* Sacc. This serious malady shows as black spots on the leaves, a black rot on the fruit and a blackening and canker on the young stem. The French name is *Charbon*, which is the equivalent of the Greek *Anthrax*. Plant pathologists, especially in U.S.A., have extended the meaning of the term to include all diseases caused by *Sphaceloma, Gloeosporium, Colletotrichum*, and other members of the Melanconieae (p. 76).

Towards the end of the season spots on infected leaves which remain on the plant join up and form irregular bright brown patches surrounded by a dark marginal line ; the greater part of the leaf may be occupied.

On the stem dull brown cankers are formed which become whitish or greyish white in the centre. They are much smaller than the lesions on the leaves, being about a twelfth of an inch wide ; they are circular or elongated with the long axis parallel to that of the stem. Usually the surface is raised, but occasionally it is depressed at the centre. When there are several lesions these may become confluent and so form a larger irregular area.

The appearance on hips and peduncles resembles that on the leaves ; on calyx lobes that on the stems.

The fruit-body of the fungus is a compact layer of hyphae bearing oval hyaline spores at their tips. There is no definite wall. The fruit-bodies (*acervuli*) are sometimes prominent and concentrically arranged, but at others are difficult to make out even with a lens. The fungus was previously known as *Phyllosticta Rosarum* Passerini, but *Phyllosticta* has a definite pycnidial wall.

All affected parts should be removed and burned, and the plant sprayed with colloidal cuprous oxide or ammoniacal copper carbonate. If the attack is severe the spraying should be repeated every ten days. No infected leaves or parts of stem should be left on the ground.

DOWNY MILDEW or BLACK MILDEW

(*Peronospora sparsa* Berk.)

Young Rose plants under glass frequently begin to wilt for no obvious reason and the leaflets fall in showers when the branch is slightly shaken. On the upper surface of the leaves irregular brown or brownish purple spots are seen, and on the lower surface corresponding to them are small whitish grey powdery fungal tufts. These are the conidiophores of *Peronospora sparsa*, one of the Phycomycetes. The spores (conidia) are comparatively large and serve for the rapid dissemination of the fungus. Owing to the extension of the fungal hyphae in the tissues the brown spots extend rapidly and the leaves shrivel up and soon fall. The sepals may also be attacked. The fungus spreads to the stem, first forming there elongated, sunken, dark brown patches. The whole plant may eventually droop and die. When the disease is not serious enough to kill the plants, blooming is delayed for two or three weeks. The disease rarely occurs out of doors in this country, but has been recorded as severely attacking seedling briars and adjacent bushes. In glass houses it occasionally assumes an epidemic form and causes considerable loss. When it infects a house its spread is remarkably rapid and destructive. It appears to be associated with poor aeration, excessive humidity, and high temperatures during the day and low temperatures at night.

The resting spores (oospores) of the fungus (p. 73, Fig. F) have been recorded from the Continent. They are somewhat larger than the conidia and, unlike them, possess a thick, stratified and folded brown wall.

The disease is controlled by proper ventilation and regulation of humidity and temperature, and frequent spraying with colloidal cuprous oxide or colloidal sulphur. Vaporising with sulphur has also been successful.

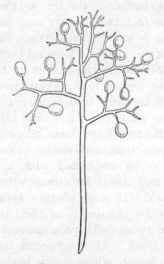

Peronospora sparsa Berk.: Conidiophore bearing conidia.
Magnification, 225.

CANKER AND " DIE BACK "

Canker in Roses has proved as troublesome to assign to the various causal fungi as it is to the grower. For some time there was confusion with the lesions of Crown Gall (p. 121), and even after certain fungi were implicated many growers regarded the original lesion as due to frost injury with the fungus as a saprophyte growing on the dead tissue. Although such saprophytic fungi occasionally occur there is now proof that several parasitic species may produce cankers. So far as the grower is concerned the fact that canker may be caused by different fungi is of little importance, for the treatment for all is the same. Though it is often possible to distinguish between the lesions by their general appearance on nearly related varieties of Rose, it is not so where there is difference in stem form and structure. The popular names already in use for canker diseases have been adopted here, but it has not been thought advisable to coin others.

Canker is often associated with a dying back of the stem, and this is sometimes wrongly referred to as Die Back. In some plants a specific parasite is responsible for the death, at their tips, of stem, branches and twigs, with progressive killing downwards ; Die Back is then a specific disease. This is not so in Roses, where dying back of stems is very common and is due to many causes. Frequently the tips are injured by frost ; there may be lack of water and a wilting followed by death ; or a deficiency or excess of nutrient salts in the soil. Fungi which are normally saprophytic, growing on this dead portion may pass along into the living tissues and destroy them. The fact that a fungus grows and fruits on such dead stems is not a proof that it has caused their destruction.

Dying back is often a secondary effect of a disease. It frequently follows a severe attack of a Stem Canker which, by encircling the stem, prevents the passage of water to the parts above it. Further, the defoliation consequent on some diseases in their acute form, *e.g.*, Black Spot, so weakens the plant that it is less able to withstand the attacks of fungi which are only facultative parasites : a dying back of the tips is a common result.

Roses seem particularly prone to damage from fungi gaining entrance *via* snags of all sorts left after the removal of flower, fruit or branch, and through wounds after pruning, or from thorns or hail, or through dead buds and leaf scars, insect punctures, or even lesions caused by other fungi, as, for example, Stem Canker following Rust or *vice versa*.

STEM CANKER

(Leptosphaeria Coniothyrium (Fuckel) Sacc.,
Coniothyrium Fuckelii Sacc.)

This is the commonest Stem Canker and the most destructive. Infection takes place through wounds or dormant buds on stems and twigs of all ages, very often at the cut end after pruning. The first symptom is slightly yellowish or reddish, spotted and streaked, pimply or water-soaked areas which become brown, sunken and cracked. They continue to increase in size and adjacent areas often become confluent. The discoloration frequently extends all round the stems for several inches, usually being separated from the healthy tissue by a reddish border. When once cracks have appeared a wound callus is produced and large irregular cankers result. The fruit-bodies of the fungus soon appear as minute black spots on the surface of the lesion and often cover the canker.

Coniothyrium Fuckelii Sacc.: Section of pycnidium.
Magnification, 225.

Fig. 14.

Snags left after bad pruning, infected by one of the fungi,
causing a " die-back." This plant was dead a month after this
photograph was taken.

The commonest form is the pycnidium. This is flask-shaped with a well-marked dark brown wall and an apical opening. The brown elliptical spores are formed by the budding of the innermost layer of cells which line the inside of the pycnidial wall. It is the abundance of these spores, just below the surface, which gives a sooty appearance. The perfect stage of the fungus, *Leptosphaeria Coniothyrium* (Fuckel) Sacc., has a similar structure to that of the pycnidial stage, but is a perithecium enclosing asci with eight, brownish three-septate spores. This Pyrenomycete is somewhat rare on Roses, but frequent on raspberry and blackberry stems and a wide range of hosts.

Diseased stems should be cut back as soon as the disease is noticed. In its early stages it is not very harmful, but if allowed to proceed to the canker stage it often kills the plant. The fungus is so common in some districts that fruit-bodies may be formed on the inner margin of the epidermis at the end of almost every pruned stem : disease results only when infection occurs along the stem. All sprays so far tried are ineffective in controlling the disease.

BRAND CANKER

(*Coniothyrium Wernsdorffiae* Laubert)

This canker, first recorded from Germany, and apparently very rare in this country, causes considerable losses in U.S.A. The name Brand Canker is given to the disease because of the blackened areas on the stem in early spring, which look as if they had been burned. They begin as small reddish spots and as they increase in size become darker with a somewhat more definite margin. The cells at the centre of the spot are killed and become light brown with a reddish brown or purple margin usually surrounded by an indefinite reddish area standing out in marked contrast to the green of the stem. Fruit-bodies (pycnidia) appear as minute elevations, and as they increase in size their protruding necks cause small longitudinal splits in the bark exposing a black mass of spores. In the second year a wound callus usually forms and a typical canker develops.

The fungus gains entrance through wounds or dormant buds on stems at least a year old. Infection usually takes place in late winter or early spring during the period when Rose stems are often protected at their base with soil or leaves. Plants left without such covering are rarely severely attacked. When the lesions are well developed before the winter covering is removed, they become black ; after being exposed for a fortnight or so they assume the normal appearance.

The wounds are often confluent, dark bands alternating with brown diseased tissue a foot or more along the stem. They vary in size and, if they occur early in the year, may girdle the stem and cause the dying back of the parts above ; later girdling usually results in the formation of a gall, often two inches in diameter, above the wound, the stem also sometimes increasing in size.

Only the pycnidial form of *Coniothyrium Wernsdorffiae* is known. It closely resembles *C. Fuckelii*, but differs in the larger size of its fruit-bodies and spores and in its cultural characters. It is apparently confined to Roses.

Diseased stems should be cut out. No control has been obtained in America by treating with fungicides, but almost complete control by leaving Roses uncovered during the winter.

BROWN CANKER

(*Diaporthe umbrina* Jenkins, *Cryptosporella umbrina* (Jenk.) Jenk. & Wehmeyer)

This disease is widely spread in America, where it was first noticed, and is one of the most important in the Eastern States. In recent years it has been found several times in this country.

On young stems small circular reddish spots appear which later become whitish necrotic lesions. Often the spots are so numerous and crowded that they form white patches. During winter and spring conspicuous brightly coloured cankers develop about some of the white spots and may eventually reach several inches in length, frequently girdling the stem which results in the death of the parts above. The cankers have a light chestnut-brown centre sometimes surrounded by a deep purple border, though the margin is generally defined only by the difference in colour between the normal and cankered portions. Scattered over the surface of the lesions may be seen the projecting necks of a fungus. This is a Pyrenomycete with its perithecia clustered below a light brown mass of compact hyphae (*stroma*), through which they push their short stout necks to the surface. The ascospores are hyaline, one-celled but occasionally pseudo-septate. The fungus was originally described as *Diaporthe* in the mistaken belief that the spores

112

PLATE X.

CHLOROSIS

were immature and that they would later become septate.

The pycnidial stage is a *Phomopsis*. The spores (*a* spores) are extruded as light yellowish brown coils in damp weather. Conidia are also sometimes formed in cavities in the stroma. The canker may occur on any portion of the stem or branches.

The fungus apparently sometimes gains entrance into the tissue through wounds, but at other times no trace of external injury can be seen. Whenever the fungus is established it advances rapidly, producing the characteristic lesions. It is probable that the ascospores live over the winter in the old canker and produce early spring infection.

The flowers are not infrequently attacked by a pycnidial fungus with a resulting conspicuous discoloration. This is now considered to belong to *Diaporthe eres*, a species which attacks many different hosts and which on Roses has been called *Diaporthe incarcerata*.

Cankered stems should be cut away and burned. After the plants have become dormant in autumn they should be sprayed with Bordeaux mixture and again in early spring. Later in the year colloidal cuprous oxide should be substituted.

DIE-BACK

(*Gnomonia Rubi* Rehm)

An extensive die-back of Rambler Roses due to the fungus *Gnomonia Rubi* was first described from the Royal Horticultural Society's Gardens at Wisley, but has since been observed in many parts of the country. It occurs also on wild Rose, bramble and loganberry.

Long shoots become black and dead, and leaves of others turn yellow and fall. Here and there ashen grey areas, several inches long, occur, usually between the black portions and the healthy green tissues, the grey areas being separated from the green by a vivid reddish purple area, which, though diseased, is still living. The grey areas invariably bear remains of one or more dead buds, and the epidermis is cracked in several places. The disease spreads slowly until the shoots are killed down to the ground level.

Numerous papillae develop on the grey areas, and later grow out as hair-like projections. These are the necks of small flask-like structures (perithecia), which contain septate spores in asci. There are not invariably eight of these, as is usual in Ascomycetes, but they vary from five to eight, six being most frequent, with four larger than the remainder.

114

Inoculations with the fungus from bramble bring about infection and subsequent die-back in Rambler Roses and wild Roses. The spores are liberated at the time when the buds are beginning to open, and it is probable that infection takes place through the dead tissue of buds killed by frost.

All diseased shoots should be cut out and burned. Spraying with Bordeaux mixture or colloidal cuprous oxide when the buds are just bursting would probably help in controlling the disease.

GNOMONIA ROSAE *Fuckel*

Another Rose disease due to a species of *Gnomonia* has been recorded from the Continent. During the summer faded olive-brown patches appear on the borders of leaves and gradually spread, but usually the leaf falls before the whole surface is covered. When one of the spots on the leaf is sectioned and examined under the microscope no spores are to be seen, although mycelium is massed in the upper epidermal cells and in the walls; it is usually confined to the inter-cellular spaces in the palisade tissue and mesophyll of the leaf. In spite of the heavy infection the leaf tissues appear to be little altered.

About two months or so after the fall of the leaf, hair-like emergences may be seen somewhat regularly dispersed over its upper surface. These are the protruding necks of the fruit-bodies (perithecia) of the fungus, which are immersed in the tissues of the leaf occupying practically its whole cross section and often causing it to bulge on each surface. The perithecium has a well developed wall, and massed within its cavity are numerous asci containing eight spindle-shaped, colourless spores with a wall across the middle where they are sometimes slightly constricted. The destroying of infected leaves and spraying with a copper fungicide will keep the disease in check.

GRIPHOSPHAERIA CORTICOLA *(Fuckel) v.*
Hoehn.
(METASPHAERIA CORTICOLA (Fuckel) Sacc.)

This fungus causes a canker of Rose stems and apparently does not affect other parts. It is common on wild Roses and occurs also on *Rubus, Crataegus, Prunus* and other genera.

The canker begins as a brown depression in the green bark, frequently around a dead bud, thorn scar, Rust lesion, pruning wound, or other kind of injury. Its margin is smooth and purplish.

The canker usually extends about half way round the stem and ranges from half an inch to several inches in length. As the bark dies numerous small blackish fructifications develop. With cessation of growth the bark becomes sunken, but the wood is not exposed and the margin does not become rough and swollen as with *Coniothyrium Fuckelii*. Occasionally the canker completely girdles the stem causing the portion above to die back. If cankers or stems killed by the fungus are allowed to remain on the plant the disease spreads rather rapidly by secondary infection from spores.

The first fruit-bodies are conidial. They are sunk in the substratum and become partly exposed on the rupture of the tissue. The most usual form is an acervulus with no definite wall : the brown, elliptical, three-septate spores arise from a pad of fungal tissue. This is *Coryneum* (*Coryneopsis*) *microstictum*, which is frequently reported as affecting Roses. Sometimes there is a definite pycnidial wall which places it in the form-genus *Hendersonia*. The perfect stage is a perithecium, also sunk in the substratum, with a tapering neck which becomes visible on the rupture of the over-lying tissue. The spores are hyaline, spindle shaped, and mostly have three septa. The fungus is usually placed in *Metasphaeria*, but a new genus, *Griphosphaeria*, has been proposed for it because of the peculiar character of the perithicial wall, most of which is formed of two layers of closely compressed parallel hyphae, the inner hyaline, the outer brown.

Diseased stems should be cut out and burned. Spraying is not efficacious as a control.

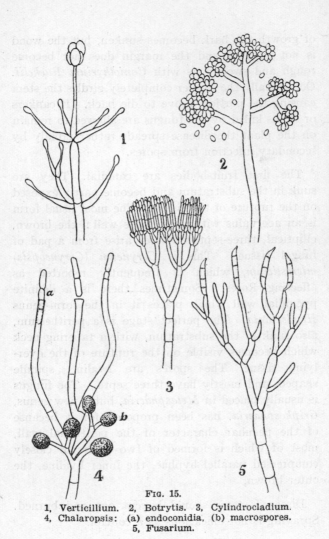

FIG. 15.

1, Verticillium. 2, Botrytis. 3, Cylindrocladium.
4, Chalaropsis: (a) endoconidia. (b) macrospores.
5, Fusarium.

BOTRYTIS CINEREA *Fr.*

This is the " grey mould " so prevalent on decaying vegetation of all kinds where it forms dense grey velvety tufts which later become brownish. These tufts are composed of upright hyphae, which branch and bear grape-like clusters of oval spores, each attached to a minute projection (Fig. 15, 2). Much smaller conidia (*microconidia*) are also formed.

Usually the fungal hyphae on and in the sub-stratum become compacted into hard masses (*sclerotia*) with a black surface. They may be less than the size of a pin head or reach half an inch in length.

Botrytis cinerea may occasionally act as a parasite : such facultative parasitism is not an unusual phenomenon and many different kinds of plant may be affected. Thus *Botrytis* frequently attacks crops, vegetables and horticultural plants in the open and herbaceous plants in greenhouses.

Botrytis cinerea is composed of many strains, but so far as is known all appear to be facultative parasites and very catholic in their choice of hosts. Invariably entrance is gained into a plant through dead or delicate tissues.

In some years, particularly when the season is wet, *Botrytis* causes much damage to Roses. It most frequently occurs on the dead ends of branches, particularly those which have been exposed to

119

cold winds and frost, and, invading the living tissue, kills it, usually to the next active internode. In autumn and winter, however, when active growth of the Rose has ceased, the fungus may pass right down the stem and eventually kill it. Even when no growth of the mould is apparent, the disease can be recognised by the cortex becoming a characteristically uniform dark brown, with no trace of red or purple. The fungus can infect any wound or damage of stem, leaf or bloom. Any snag or dead wood, any faded or old unexpanded bloom is liable to be the source of attack.

In addition to Stem Canker, the dying back of stems and the killing of young shoots, flower stalks may rot or flower buds be seriously damaged or destroyed in damp weather or when soil conditions are unfavourable. Sometimes opened blooms are affected (" petal fire "). This occasionally occurs on the outer petals of cut Roses boxed for market, appearing as small circular brown spots with a darker brown margin on yellow and pink blooms, and as colourless or water-soaked-like spots on red ones. They are due to spores which are present on the petals germinating in the confined moist atmosphere of the boxes, and growing on the tissue of the petals.

All affected parts of the plant should be removed and burned. Calcium bisulphite appears to be a specific for *Botrytis*. Dormant plants should be sprayed with a two per cent. solution, growing plants with a one per cent.

120

CROWN GALL

(*Bacterium tumefaciens* E.F.Sm. & Townsend)

The galls or swellings which occur usually at or near the ground level on Rose stems have been in the past attributed to various causes. It is now known that they are caused by a species of bacterium (*Bacterium tumefaciens*). Crown gall is a disease which has been recorded from all over the world occurring on a great variety of cultivated plants and on some wild ones.

In Roses the galls become quite hard and woody and more or less cracked or irregular at the surface when old. They vary greatly in size ; in some Rose stocks they may be more than 50 per cent. of the total weight. Though most frequent at the collar the galls may occur on any part of the root or shoot and are not at all uncommon on branches. Most varieties of Roses are susceptible to tumour formation, but the character of the infection which follows depends upon whether the plant is growing rapidly or is partially dormant. Well nourished rapidly growing plants produce much larger tumours than slowly growing ones.

The cells of the part of the Rose attacked are not disintegrated and killed, but are stimulated to rapid multiplication. The effect of the bacterial stimulus produces a growth resembling in every way the callus growths arising as a result of wounding.

121

By many the presence of galls is not regarded as being detrimental to a plant, but from the large size they frequently attain it is obvious that they must absorb material which has been elaborated for other purposes. Stunted growth is not, however, so common a result in Roses as in many other plants.

It was only after much research that the causal organism of crown gall was isolated. *Bacterium tumefaciens* is a small, white, motile, rod-shaped organism with polar flagella. It has not been possible to demonstrate the presence of the bacteria within the cells of the gall by staining. Sometimes at least, the bacteria, which are first located on the wounded surface, and to some extent also in the vessels and adjoining intercellular spaces of the cortex, are later present as a film on the rough exterior of the gall. Secondary galls are often produced, but these apparently are always due to the migration of the bacteria, which form new centres of pathological disturbance. By cross-inoculations it has been found that though there are differences in the virulence of different isolations there are only two or three well-marked strains.

So far as is known infection of the host always takes place through wounds.

The only effective treatment is to cut away the gall. The resulting wounded surface should be smeared with Stockholm tar to prevent re-infection and the attack of fungi. *Coniothyrium Fuckelii* often occurs on broken down galls or on the wounds left after their excision.

GRAFT DISEASE

(*Coniothyrium Rosarum* Cooke & Harkness)

A serious disease of Roses which attacks the plants immediately after grafting, during the period in which they are kept in a warm moist atmosphere for the hastening of callus formation, was first described in U.S.A., but is not uncommon in this country. The fungus causing the disease is very similar to that of Stem Canker (*Coniothyrium Fuckelii*) p. 108, and, indeed, they are regarded by some mycologists as the same species. The characteristic symptom is the occurrence of lesions on the scion at, or just above the union, which results in the sudden wilting and death of the young Rose graft. These lesions appear first as light yellow water-soaked areas, but as the tissues are killed they become dark brown. As the sub-epidermal tissues die the epidermis becomes loosened and changes colour from dark to light brown. The pycnidia of the fungus develop on the light brown areas, fruiting there a comparatively short time after the death of the tissue and producing an abundance of spores. The leaves of the young shoots wilt and drop.

The lesions usually encircle the scion within a few days, so that the death of the graft is sudden. Sometimes, however, the wound extends up the stem as a narrow furrow ; the graft does not die, but gives rise to a dwarfed one-sided plant which may live for several years, developing cankers, which may include a half or more of the stem, and which serve as a constant source of infection. In plants two or three years old infection of the open wounds left by pruning or by cutting flowers may occur. The fungus grows down the stem on all sides, but rarely spreads more than three or four inches.

The destructiveness of the fungus depends upon its rate of travel in the tissues. Among the factors which influence this are the suitability of the stock for the particular scion employed and the speed at which they become connected.

Certain other fungi have been reported as causing damage to stems of cultivated Roses in this country. Among these are : **Didymella sepincoliformis** (de Not.) Sacc., causing wilt and death of young lateral and terminal shoots in spring. The wilt is followed by the appearance of scattered brown pycnidia. Perithecia later develop in large numbers showing as black dots in the bark surrounded by a white zone where the epidermis has torn away. The fungus also occurs on wild Roses.

Botryosphaeria Dothidea (Fr.) Ces. & de Not. is common on wild Roses and is known as " Briar Scab." It sometimes severely attacks cultivated Roses, forming black raised masses of stroma on the stem, frequently around the thorns, with light concentric markings. The perithecia are sunk in the stroma.

CROWN CANKER

(*Cylindrocladium scoparium* Morgan)

A disease which has been given the name Crown Canker* was first described as causing loss in flower production under glass in America, and has occasionally been troublesome in this country. Plants are usually attacked at, or just above, the union of scion and stock, the lesion frequently encircling the stem and advancing from ground level to several inches above the soil. The roots are also affected, sometimes the whole root system being involved. The first indication of the disease is a slight discoloration of the bark. As the disease advances the colour rapidly deepens to black, and the tissue appears as if soaked with water. The irregular lesions have at first a somewhat sharply defined margin, but as they increase in size the transition between healthy and diseased portions is not so well marked. Cracks soon appear in the bark and extend into the wood. At a later stage a swelling occurs at, and above, the infected area, the cracks meanwhile becoming deeper and more evident. Old lesions lose their black, water-soaked appearance. The powdery consistency of the diseased tissue, especially that underground, is

---

* The name Crown Canker, although descriptive, is not perhaps the best that could have been chosen as it is liable to be confused with either Stem Canker or Crown Gall—two diseases, moreover, which have often been confused both in name and in symptoms.

very noticeable. Most suckers developing from the root of diseased plants are yellow and straggly, being damaged at the point of attachment to the main stem.

The fungus is a weak parasite, and diseased plants do not succumb but linger on with a gradually diminishing yield of blossoms. It is practically impossible to force such plants with fertilizers. Infected plants frequently have light green leaves. Moisture plays an important part in determining the degree of severity of the attack. Both grafted plants and those growing on their own roots are affected, and no variety appears to be immune.

The causal organism is *Cylindrocladium scoparium*, a Hyphomycetous fungus. The general basic structure somewhat resembles that of some species of *Penicillium* (p. 118, Fig. 15, 3). The spores are, however, borne singly and not in chains. They are large, cylindrical, hyaline and one-septate, the spore-mass being held together by a sticky slime.

The spread of the disease is apparently lessened by having graft unions above the soil. Soil sterilisation and the use of healthy stock and scions for grafting is the only feasible method of control.

Cylindrocladium scoparium has been reported as causing a shoot wilt in varieties of plum and cherry used for root stocks.

BLACK MOULD OF GRAFTS

(*Chalaropsis thielavioides* Peyronel)

In the Eastern U.S.A. in recent years severe damage has been caused to Roses in grafting frames by a disease which prevents the formation of callus and the " taking " of grafts, resulting in the death of the scion. The losses are always heavy, sometimes reaching a hundred per cent.

Newly infected Rose grafts show a white to greyish white mildew-like growth over the surfaces of both stock and scion. This later becomes darker grey, olive-green to brown, and finally black. The stem becomes brown above the union and the discoloration may spread upwards ; discoloration may also occur in the stocks.

The fungus shows two kinds of spores, endoconidia and macroconidia. The first to appear are the endoconidia, which are formed within the end cells of conidiophores and expelled through the apex (p. 118, Fig. 15, 4a). The conidiophores, consisting of three or four cells, are upright and taper upwards, being connected by rather short hyphal threads ; they are white then greenish. The endoconidia are produced in great abundance and often cling together, so that there may be twenty or more in a chain. At first they are cylindrical and hyaline, later they are more or less oval and green. The macroconidia are larger and borne singly and

127

terminally on short conidiophores, or sessile. Usually they are formed in grape-like clusters. Their wall is thick and eventually dark brown (Fig. 15, 4b). The fungus is able to penetrate any wound surface, as, for example, the cut ends of branches, and may make considerable headway before any discoloration is seen. It may occur on roots, but does not cause a typical root rot.

The mycelium passes from cell to cell, travelling most rapidly through the vessels, but growing only slowly in the cortex, which is much discoloured ; the pith and medullary rays are not changed to the same degree.

The disease is mainly confined to grafted plants. It has been reported chiefly from Manetti stocks, which were apparently healthy on arrival. The obvious method of control is to use only uncontaminated stock, making certain of this by previous disinfection.

Though *Chalaropsis thielavioides* has not been recorded as affecting Roses here, it is possible that it was the fungus identified as *Thielavia basicola*, thought to be responsible for the loss of stocks some years ago in Cheshire ; this fungus also has endoconidia.

Chalaropsis thielavioides is responsible for a graft disease and root rot of walnuts in this country.

FIG. 16.

Graft disease caused by *Coniothyrium Rosarum* Cooke Harkness.
The fungus gains entrance through wounds at ground level,
and slowly kills the plant.

SILVER-LEAF

(*Stereum purpureum* (Fr.) Fr.)

Silver-leaf is a common disease of plants, more particularly of trees of the family Rosaceae. It is characterised by the silvery or leaden appearance of leaves followed by their fading, and the death of the tree or bush. There is no sign of the fungus causing the disease until after the damage is done, when brown or brownish purple fruit-bodies of *Stereum purpureum* appear on the dead portions. These are about three inches or so across, flat and closely attached when the substratum is horizontal, but imbricated when it is vertical, the upper surface then being hairy; the spore-bearing surface (*hymenium*) is lilac or purplish. The colour of the fungus is brighter when moist, and fades with age.

Silver-leaf is not common in Roses, but occasionally occurs, especially on Ramblers. The silvering of the leaves is not always well marked in Roses, for this appearance is due to the epidermal cells breaking away and leaving an air space through which light is refracted, and thin leaves hardly show it before they fade and fall.

Stereum purpureum is a common saprophyte as well as a destructive parasite, and may often be seen on old stumps and on fences. Very occasionally it fruits on dead branches of living Roses : the removal of such branches will probably save the plant.

Roses attacked by *Stereum purpureum* rarely survive. They should be dug up and burned.

129

L

ROOT DISEASES

Roses are remarkably free from specific root diseases. Sometimes in glass houses *Fusarium* causes extensive browning and death of roots, particularly the younger ones ; the signs above ground are that the leaves become blotchy, wilt and fall prematurely. *Fusarium* is a mould (*Hypho-mycete*) with sickle-shaped septate spores (Fig. 15, 5). Many species are common saprophytes in the soil, but are liable to attack plants which are in a weakened state on account of unsuitable soil conditions such as excessive moisture and lack of aeration.

Rose growers in America are occasionally troubled with similar attacks by species of the mould *Ver-ticillium*, which cause wilting ; a wilt due to *Verticillium alboatrum*, which produces wilt disease in a large number of plants, has been reported in this country. *Verticillium* is a Hyphomycete in which the conidiophores with terminal hyaline simple conidia are arranged in whorls along an upright stalk (Fig. 15, 1).

Roses in the open rarely suffer from root diseases. Occasionally, however, and chiefly in newly-made beds, white, cottony mycelial strands of fungi of the toadstool type invade the soil and intermingle with the roots, apparently interfering with the activities of the root hairs and sometimes massing into a white membrane-like layer on roots and rootlets damaged in transplanting. There seems to be no definite parasitism and the trouble usually disappears the following season if routine treatment of the beds has been carried out.

The mycelia are those of common saprophytes such as *Collybia dryophila*, *Stropharia aeruginosa* and *Hypholoma fasciculare*.

HONEY-TUFT

(*Armillaria mellea* (Vahl) Fr.)

This toadstool occasionally causes the death of Roses, particularly Climbers. Although the fungus may grow saprophytically it is a serious disease of trees and shrubs.

In the early stages of attack on Roses the stem, or root, show, on sectioning, that the mycelium has penetrated the tissues as white membranous sheets extending parallel to the surface. The leaves soon become sickly and fall and the plant dies. Sometimes before this happens, but usually afterwards, the fruit-bodies of the fungus may appear on or in close proximity to the base of the stem. They are usually in clusters. The cap is honey-colour, but may be paler or darker, up to four inches or so across and marked with small squamules which are mostly clustered about the centre. The gills are whitish then pinkish and often spotted, and join the stem more or less at right angles. The stem is stout, coloured like the cap, but becoming blackish with age ; towards the top there is a large, white, persistent ring with a yellow border.

The fungus spreads by means of *rhizomorphs*. These are compacted masses of fungal threads which have a black surface and look like flattened leather boot laces, often branched and anastomosing, sometimes forming a loose network. They can travel considerable distances through the soil, either from old stumps or infected trees and shrubs.

Diseased plants should be uprooted and the soil well dug, removing any rhizomorphs which may be seen after tracing them to their source.

ROESLERIA HYPOGAEA *Thum. & Pass.*

This fungus is chiefly known on account of its association with a root rot of grapes, but has been recorded from a large number of host plants, including Roses. The fruits of the fungus occur throughout the year, but particularly in autumn. They appear usually in clusters, each consisting of a straight or flexuous, white or greenish yellow stalk, with a more or less globose, whitish, then greyish or greenish, villose head, the whole being somewhat less than a quarter of an inch high. The head is composed of a number of asci, interspersed with projecting paraphyses, which give it a woolly appearance. The ascospores are hyaline and spherical, though occasional ones are flattened and slightly disc-shaped. There is still considerable difference of opinion about whether or not *Roesleria* is parasitic, though it has been shown that when the ascospores are sown in wounds the fungus can establish itself in the tissues of living roots. The mycelium which develops is felty in appearance and light to dull green. The fruit-body is apparently produced only on dead roots.

" CHLOROSIS "

Chlorosis in medicine is " green sickness," a disease principally affecting young women, one of the characteristic symptoms being a pale or greenish complexion ; in plants it also denotes colour change, paradoxically the loss of green in leaves and stem.

Chlorosis is often one of the symptoms of disease. Many plant diseases were at one time regarded as physiological as no causal agent was known. Most of these have now been shown to be due to viruses. It is most convenient in Roses to restrict chlorosis as the name for a disease which appears to be entirely due to a disturbance of the physiology of the plant and in no way attributable to a parasite. Albino seedlings are excluded as they are definitely pathological. The inherited tendency to produce variegated leaves which is seen in healthy plants of many horticultural varieties, and occasionally in Roses, is not usually regarded as pathological, for such variegated plants have sufficient green leaf surface to supply their needs.

VIRUS

Virus diseases of Roses have received little attention in this country. Rose Mosaic has been noted from time to time, but does not seem to be very common in cultivated varieties. The symptoms of mosaic are a mottling of the leaves, either lighter and darker green, or green and yellow, very occasionally white. There may also be a twisting of the midrib and the whole plant may be dwarfed and the flowers pale and imperfect on shortened stems.

It is probable that closer search will reveal other virus diseases.

In the U.S.A. three distinct mosaic diseases ("infectious chlorosis") have been described. The commonest is Rose Mosaic I or White's Rose Mosaic, which has brought severe losses to growers of Roses under glass.

There is also the Rose Streak Virus, which causes reddish brown ring patterns on leaves, and green or brownish ring markings on stems.

A virus disease with symptoms of wilt and die-back has been described in Australia.

Virus Mosaic of Roses is not sap transferable by insects. Thus White's Rose Mosaic does not spread under glass, and a diseased plant may be left amongst healthy ones without fear of infection. But the virus is systemic and occurs throughout the plant. It is carried in buds, cuttings and scions taken from infected plants.

The fact that there were infectious diseases caused by ultra-microscopic viruses was only gradually realised. The later recognition of the economic importance of virus diseases led to a vast volume of research and an abundance of theory about how the virus acts. There is still much doubt about the true nature of these " organisms." In recent years a number of viruses have been obtained in crystalline form. They have been photographed in the plant cell by the electron microscope shadow technique, and their apparent sizes have been estimated in various ways.

CHLOROSIS
(See Colour Plate X.)

Chlorosis in Roses is not uncommon in some districts, its symptoms being that the leaves gradually lose their green colour and become a sickly yellow. Usually it appears towards the end of spring, beginning frequently between the veins and along the borders of the younger leaves ; the stem also shows yellow patches, which become confluent. Generally the whole of the leaf becomes yellow, but occasionally some parts remain green, and a speckled appearance results. The leaves shrivel and fall, and the plant produces weedy shoots and a crop of stunted leaves before it finally collapses. Owing to the non-development of the green colouring matter the leaves are unable to perform their function of building up food material. With the cessation of carbon assimilation the plant starves to death ; no flowering plant wholly without

135

chlorophyll can continue to live—leaving out of account those bizarre plants which have taken to parasitic and saprophytic habits.

There are several types of chlorosis. The common type affecting Roses is sometimes known as " lime chlorosis." It is well marked in many plants, and has caused much concern to the French wine-growing industry owing to its prevalence on American vine stocks in certain districts.

It is known from experiment that the presence of iron in an available form in the soil is necessary for the formation of chlorophyll ; nitrogen and magnesium are also required for its production.

The factors which lead to iron deficiency are very complex, being both external and internal to the plant. It is doubtful whether any soil is really deficient in the small amount of iron required. In calcareous soils there is a depression in the amount of available iron : it has been suggested that this is brought about by the action of calcium carbonate on the iron forming ferric carbonate, but another view is that lime-induced chlorosis is not a result of the iron being locked up in the soil, but that there is a disturbance of the physiological balance in the living cells after the iron has entered the plant. Iron deficiency may also be the result of an excess of some other element, especially manganese. It may also result from a lack of other mineral elements, usually potassium.

Excessive moisture apparently increases the severity of the disease.

136

Iron deficiency has proved the most difficult to correct in crop plants. Sulphate of iron usually arrests chlorosis of Roses if added to the soil at the rate of an ounce for each plant. It is best applied as crystals about the size of a pea and should be lightly pricked in about the roots. Spraying with a solution of an ounce of iron sulphate to a gallon of water often turns the leaves green. It is a good plan to combine the two methods until the symptoms disappear. If the soil is alkaline it should be treated with sulphur.

In woody plants, such as fruit trees, some iron salt (sulphate, citrate or phosphate) is placed in holes bored in the trunk, and sealed with wax. Mostly a cure is effected within a fortnight.

Much attention has been given in recent years to the nutritional requirements of plants, and it has been shown that, in addition to the major elements, nitrogen, phosphorus, calcium, magnesium, potassium and sulphur, which are needed in relatively large quantity, there are minor elements which are just as necessary for normal growth. So far as is known these trace elements or micronutrients comprise iron, manganese, copper, boron and molybdenum. Some other elements are beneficial, but are not physiologically essential.

Though in Roses it is the chlorosis occurring on calcareous soils, due to iron deficiency, which is the most important and therefore the best known, there are other kinds which are due either to deficiency or to excess of other elements. The effects of these have been studied in fruit trees and crops, and doubtless research will soon be extended to Roses and other horticultural plants. Soils having marked mineral deficiencies have been noted and methods of treatment devised. Presumably the results obtained are common knowledge to gardeners in the areas affected. It will therefore be sufficient to say that deficiency in the trace elements manganese, copper, zinc and molybdenum may be marked by a greater or lesser amount of chlorosis ; and that excess of copper, zinc, nickel, cobalt and chromium also produce chlorosis, this being largely or wholly the result of induced iron deficiency.

SOOTY MOULD

(*Fumago* sp.)

Roses do not suffer so frequently from Sooty Mould as do many other wild and cultivated plants. At times, however, the leaves show the characteristic appearance—a black sooty layer which peels off in flakes during hot weather. The whole of the upper surface of the leaf may be covered. The black substance is formed of a dense intermingled mass of dark coloured mycelia of several fungi, the most usual genus being *Fumago*—one of the Hyphomycetes. The fungal hyphae in no way penetrate into the leaf tissues and consequently derive no nourishment from the plant, but subsist upon the " honey dew " deposited by Aphides,

Scale Insects and Mealy Bugs. It is apparent, therefore, that leaves are disfigured in this way only when these pests are present ; if these are kept in check Sooty Mould does not appear.

BRONZING

The leaves of certain varieties of Roses, especially those of young plants forced under glass, often show bronze mottled patches with a yellow border. The leaves so affected drop off, and the plant is consequently more or less starved, as well as being unattractive in appearance. Bronzing generally appears on new branches below where blooms have been removed. The main cause of the trouble seems to be over-feeding.

MISTLETOE

(*Viscum album* L. var. *Mali* Tubeuf)

Research on the mistletoe has shown that in Europe this interesting species of flowering plant comprises three races or varieties. One of these, *Viscum album* var. *Mali*, occurs on broad-leaved plants, principally willow, poplar, beech and hazel, but occasionally on other plants, including many rosaceous genera, amongst which is the Rose.

Part III

INSECTICIDES AND FUNGICIDES

The maintenance of health in plants is essential if the full purpose of their cultivation is to be achieved. It is, moreover, of immense importance in reducing the incidence of pest and disease organisms. Keeping a plant free from pests lessens the chances of the spread of disease, for fungal spores are carried about on the bodies of insects, and may gain entrance through the wounds made by their punctures. An active defensive attitude against pest and disease should be adopted by applying hygienic principles to plant growth and by recognising that good cultivation is the essence of prevention.

Cultural methods of control go far in attaining this end, and include good and thorough cultivation, weed destruction, judicious manuring, effective drainage, and the choice of favourable soil and site.

The factors that govern the increase of a pest are climatic and biological. The effect of favourable weather during certain stages of its life-cycle may result in a rapid increase of populations. Biological factors, however, are equally important and refer to the availability and attractiveness of its food plants, and to the presence of natural enemies. Such natural controlling agents include insectivorous birds ; predaceous insects (Ladybirds and their grubs, the larvae of Hover Flies and of Lacewing Flies, and Ground or Carabid Beetles) and other Arthropods (*e.g.*, Centipedes, Spiders and predatory Mites) ; parasites (Ichneumon-flies and related parasitic Hymenoptera, and Tachinid Flies) ; and bacterial, fungal and protozoal diseases ; all of which affect to some degree the mortality rates among insects.

Unfortunately little reliance can be placed upon these limiting factors to eradicate outbreaks of pests, owing to many reasons, and the grower must perforce take direct measures to control infestations.

Mechanical Methods include such operations as (a) Handpicking, which primitive and somewhat laborious task may still be regarded as a means of checking outbreaks in small gardens. It is employed against Leaf-Miners, Tortrix Leaf-rolling caterpillars (" Rose-Maggots "), small colonies of caterpillars, the cocoons and egg-masses of Vapourer Moth, the eggs and larvae of certain Sawflies, and the " White Grubs " of Chafers, when digging and forking the soil of infested borders.

(b) Trapping includes grease-banding the stems of standard Roses to deter ants from reaching the Aphid-infested shoots ; placing rolled pieces of sacking or corrugated-paper near plants attacked

141

by Earwigs and the nocturnally-active Otiorr-hynchus weevils; and by burying spitted potato tubers and carrots in ground infested with Wire-worms and Millepedes.

(c) Jarring refers to the shaking of branches and shoots over a beating-tray, an open inverted umbrella, or sheets of white paper, canvas or linen spread on the ground beneath the bushes to capture the diurnally-active Phyllobius weevils, and the Garden Chafer, and Pollen beetles on Rose blooms.

(d) Pruning-out shoots upon which occur the eggs of Aphides, the egg-bands and larval " tents " of the Lackey Moth, and Scale encrustations on old stems.

Chemical Methods include the operations of spraying, dusting and fumigating with chemicals in the form of liquids, solids and gases. The term " Spraying " is applied either to solutions in water (Nicotine and H E T P), suspensions in water (Lead arsenate) or to emulsions (White Oils and other emulsified washes). In Dusting, the material is applied either as a finely divided powder (Sulphur) or mixed and absorbed with a " carrier " (D D T and Nicotine dusts).

Insecticides fall into two main classes, namely, (A) Direct, and (B) Protective, but no hard and fast rules may be made concerning them, as some act on the insect both as a Contact wash and as a Stomach poison (*e.g.*, D D T).

(A) *Direct Insecticides* comprise (a) Contact Washes and (b) Ovicides. The former include

Nicotine, H E T P, Derris, Pyrethrum, and the highly refined Petroleum or White Oils, which are employed chiefly against sucking insects, including Thrips, Capsid Bugs, Leaf- and Frog-hoppers, Aphides, Scale Insects and Mealy Bugs. Such washes depend for their success upon their wetting and spreading powers, and must come into direct contact with the body of the insect. It is essential, therefore, to direct the wash to those parts of the plant upon which the pest congregates and feeds, and, in particular, the underside of the leaves and tips of the shoots.

Egg-killing washes include Tar Oils, D N O C Thiocyanate and Miscible White Oils, which kill the eggs of insects or inhibit their hatching. In addition, such washes as Tar Oils possess cleansing properties and clean the stems of growths of Algae, Lichens and Mosses. Tar Oils may be applied to Bush, Standard and Climbing Roses at concentrations of three per cent. during the dormant season to aid in controlling outbreaks of Aphides and Scales.

(B) *Protective Insecticides* include (a) Stomach or Internal Poisons (D D T and Lead arsenate), which are applied to the foliage as a cover wash or dust against leaf-eating insects, *e.g.*, Earwigs, the caterpillars of Moths, Chafer beetles, Otiorrhynchus and Phyllobius weevils, and the larvae of certain Sawflies. Care should be taken when using these washes that the spray or dust does not drip or drift on to neighbouring herb beds, to salad

143

crops and leaf vegetables, or on to ripening fruits. Furthermore, they should not be applied to plants which, when in bloom, are visited by hive bees and other pollinating insects.

(b) Repellents (Benzene hexachloride, Naphthalene and Soot) are protective in their action by repelling insects from laying their eggs on (Rose Leaf-Miner) or near their food plants (Chafers).

A further class includes Respiratory Poisons or Fumigants (Nicotine and Hydrogen cyanide), which are general glasshouse fumigants, while others are selective in their action upon pests, being toxic only to White Fly (Tetrachlorethane), Thrips (Grade 16 Naphthalene), and Red Spider Mite (Azobenzene and Naphthalene).

Soil Fumigants include Benzene hexachloride, Carbon disulphide, Naphthalene and Paradichlorobenzene, and are used primarily against soil pests, including root-infesting Aphides, Chafer and Weevil grubs, Ants and Millepedes. Some compounds serve merely as temporary repellent agents, *e.g.*, Naphthalene ; while others tend to taint root crops that are grown in the dressed ground unless an interval of several months elapses between the time of application and sowing and planting times.

Acaricides (H E T P, Lime Sulphur and Naphthalene) are compounds that possess properties against a definite group of pests, namely, Red Spider Mites.

The principles underlying control methods against fungi are the same as against insects, but though the measures to be adopted have much in common

FIG. 17.

Group of stems on left show bad pruning cuts liable to serious
infection. Stem on right properly pruned will quickly heal.

there are differences due to the different type of organism. Thus mechanical methods are impracticable except for the cutting out of diseased shoots.

As a fungal disease cannot be cured in the sense that the tissues affected can be restored to normal, all methods adopted may be regarded as preventive, either to eliminate attack or to stop its spread.

Sanitation plays a large part. In addition to the pruning out of cankers and treating the cut ends with a fungicide, all diseased foliage should be collected from the plant and from the ground and burned. Diseased leaves often crumble easily, and so the beds should be raked over and treated with a fungicide : it is advisable also to mulch the beds with grass mowings or granulated peat.

No Roses left to carry on as best they may in odd parts of a garden should be allowed to become diseased and a danger.

The main methods of combating a fungal disease are chemical—spraying and dusting.

Rose diseases are rarely so severe that the measures to be adopted are such that no regard need be paid to the appearance of the plants after treatment. Consequently in choosing a fungicide it is essential to consider whether it will cause disfigurement to the leaves or the blooms. More damage may be done to plants and houses by a fungicide than by a disease. In addition, a fungicide should adhere well and not be readily washed off by rain, it should be easily applied and should be capable of being mixed with an insecticide without serious effect on the toxicity of either component ; it should be harmless to the operator and cheap.

Rose foliage, particularly when young, is not easily wetted so " spreaders " are usually added to fungicides to obtain proper " coverage."

Fungicides which contain copper (and other heavy metals) often produce definite lesions on leaves. On those of the Rose reddish spots may form which become yellow as the cells collapse and die, and " shot-holes " may result from the falling away of the dead tissue.

Bordeaux mixture has a scorching effect on Rose leaves, and often does more harm than good, especially if the plants are drenched. Bordeaux mixture and other copper sprays have a tendency to produce harshness in the foliage, which detracts from the fresh appearance so much sought after in Roses used for decoration or for exhibition.

The problem is to procure a suitable substance which will interfere effectively with the growth of the parasite (killing the spores, or preventing sporulation, germination, or the penetration of the mycelium) and to apply it at the right spot at the most vulnerable stage of its life history. The two chief substances in use are sulphur and copper ; Homer mentioned the " pest-averting sulphur " about 1000 B.C., and copper sulphate has been in use as a fungicide since 1761 and was first employed against Rose Mildew in 1861.

In recent years colloidal or " wettable " sulphur

146

has replaced lime sulphur, which was formerly in general use by Rosarians, and the so-called " fixed " or " insoluble " coppers such as basic copper sulphate, cuprous oxide and cuprous oxychloride-sulphate, have largely replaced Bordeaux mixture.

These substances may be added to a white oil emulsion in the proportion of half an ounce to a gallon of diluted emulsion. White oil emulsion is incompatible with sulphur. Hence if it is desired to use both sulphur and copper only a water solution is practicable.

Other fungicides which have been commonly used are liver of sulphur, ammoniacal copper carbonate, malachite green, Cheshunt Compound, and arsenate of lead powder.

Copper sulphate solution is a safe winter wash (1 oz. to a gallon of water) and may be used as a soil drench.

Flowers of sulphur, green sulphur, black sulphur or other forms of sulphur for use as a dust should pass through a mesh of at least 325 to the inch. It is not necessary to apply it in such quantity as to disfigure the leaves ; indeed it need not be visible to be effective. The whole plant above ground should, however, be treated. Spores and mycelium need not necessarily be in contact with the particles of sulphur for these to be effective, as apparently the vapour given off by them is sufficient. Some complain that sulphur sometimes reduces Rose growth and especially the " breaking " of flower buds, but overtreatment by fungicides of any kind should be avoided : labour and expense are best reserved for beneficial practices.

No spraying or dusting is likely to be effective in one application. Some spores are certain to escape, and when the fungicidal substance disappears from their vicinity they are in a particularly favourable position to begin growth. Where there has been disease, spraying or dusting before the time for its reappearance is a wise precaution. Afterwards there should be repeated applications until it is certain that the main danger is over.

RULES FOR SPRAYING

The complete eradication of a pest or disease by spraying, dusting or fumigating being unachievable, the aim is to reduce the infestation or infection to a minimum, and to achieve this it is essential to use a reliable spraying or dusting machine and a suitable insecticide or fungicide.

The operation of spraying is still too often carried out in a careless manner resulting in a poor control, thus bringing criticism against the effectiveness of the materials used. Failure to achieve good results is often due to errors committed by the operator.

The following rules should be followed :—

(1) Determine correctly the pest or disease concerned in the attack and select the right type of insecticide or fungicide.

(2) Apply the wash or dust at the right time, that is, deal with the pest or disease at the stage when it is most vulnerable to attack, and never

delay applications against such pests as Aphides (Green Flies), whose rate of increase during their spring and summer phases is rapid.

(3) Direct the wash, especially Contact Washes, to that part of the plant which is parasitised. Such pests as Thrips, Leaf-hoppers and Aphides congregate and feed on the underside of the leaves ; Rust pustules are most abundant there, and thus it is essential to wet thoroughly the lower leaf surface.

(4) Do not spray in bright sunshine otherwise severe leaf scorch may result. Delay applications until after the sun's rays are off the plants or spray on dull days.

(5) Purchase all insecticides and fungicides from a reliable manufacturer, and follow the Ministry of Agriculture's official lists of approved preparations.

(6) Prepare the wash strictly according to the instructions. Ensure that it is thoroughly mixed, and is kept agitated to prevent quick precipitation (Lead arsenate) and dispersal (Oil emulsions).

(7) Strain all liquids through a sieve before use to prevent blocking of the nozzle.

(8) Use the right type of nozzle to avoid wastage of liquid. Apply thoroughly and forcefully to ensure complete wetting of the plant and insect, effective penetration to all parts of the plant, and the even distribution of cover washes (Fungicides and Stomach Poisons).

(9) Obtain an efficient spraying and dusting

machine from a reliable firm, and see that the apparatus is of sufficient size and power to cope with the amount of work to be carried out.

(10) Wash out with clear water all spraying machines immediately after use. Warm water is advisable after using oil emulsions and ovicides.

(11) Renew all washers from time to time to prevent leakages, and loosen all joints before storing the machine away.

(12) Keep all working parts of dusting and spraying machinery oiled and in good repair.

DUSTING AND SPRAYING APPLIANCES

It is essential for the successful control of Rose pests and diseases by dusting and spraying that the insecticide or fungicide is applied thoroughly by means of an efficient machine.

There are many types of appliances available, and the grower must be guided in his choice by the amount of work to be done and the size of the plants to be treated.

The type of nozzle is important, and a minimum of two nozzles is necessary. One nozzle should be fine for the application of Fungicides and Stomach poisons to provide a fairly wide-angled cone, thus producing an effective protective cover wash over the foliage ; another coarser for applying Contact Washes against sucking insects and insects' eggs to produce a penetrative wetting spray to all parts of the plants.

The Spray-arm should be fitted with an angle-bend or right-angled fitting to which the nozzles are attached. This allows the wash to be easily directed to the underside of the leaves when spraying against those pests and fungi that live on the lower surface of the foliage.

Spraying appliances range from manual pumps to power sprayers, and include :—

Hand Syringes, which may be adequate to the work required in a small garden or glasshouse, but are both wasteful and inefficient for use where a great number of plants require to be sprayed. The disadvantages are the low pressure, the wastage of material, and the loss of time in recharging.

Continuous or Double-action Hand Sprayers are far preferable to Syringes for they are fitted with a length of suction hose and give a continuous jet of spray with slow and even pumping.

Bucket Sprayers are obtainable either with a detachable pump or one that is fixed to the container. They are efficient machines when fitted with a double-action pump, but may require two operators to obtain the best results.

Knapsack Sprayers are of two types, namely, Hand-worked and Pneumatic or Compressed-air machines. Their capacities range from 1-3 gallons. The former are efficient so long as the operator does not tire of continuous pumping with an under-arm action ; the latter have the advantage that the requisite pressure (75-90 lb. per sq. in.) is obtained prior to spraying, and this allows both hands to be free to operate a lance for reaching tall plants and wall-trained Roses. Lower capacity compressed-air machines of 2-5 pints are available for use in small gardens and in glasshouses.

Wheeled Machines comprise wooden (barrel) and metal (tank) sprayers mounted on 1- or 2-wheeled carriages, and with capacities of 10-20 gallons. A wooden container has the advantage of allowing all types of washes, including acid sprays, to be used in it without injury, but the container must be kept half-full of water when not in use to prevent warping and consequent leaking.

The tank or barrel should be sufficiently clear of the ground to prevent injury to low-growing plants during its transit over cultivated borders, and the wheels should have wide rims and a large circumference for easy traction over wet and heavy ground and on dry loose soil. The fitting of pneumatic tyres is advisable to avoid " rutting " of lawns and grass paths.

Dusting Machines comprise :—

Hand-dusters, which hold from ¼-1 lb. of powder, are manipulated by means of a simple leather bellows and, when shaken, distribute the dust through a narrow spout.

Powder Dusters have a capacity of 7-14 lb. of powder, and work with a single or, preferably, double action bellows, thus providing a continuous dust cloud.

Rotary Blowers operate by means of a revolving crank-driven fan that provides a continuous and even cloud of dust, the amount of which is regulated by means of a screw control. Their capacity is 7-14 lb. of powder.

The simplest type of duster is a home-made apparatus consisting of a muslin bag to contain the dust suspended on a stick or cane which, when tapped with another stick, allows the powder to fall through the mesh on to the plants.

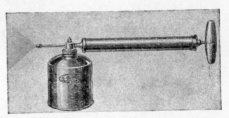

KEEP YOUR ROSES PEST-FREE!

Black Spot . . .   SHELL COPPER FUNGICIDE

Mildews . . .   SHELL DISPERSIBLE SULPHUR

Aphides. . . .   SHELL LIQUID DERRIS or
                    SHELL DERRIS WETTABLE POWDER

Chafers, Sawflies, Weevils
and Caterpillars .   SHELL 35% DDT WETTABLE POWDER or
                    SHELL 5% DDT DUST

Shell Garden Sprays offer the best
materials, packed in convenient sizes.
Easy to apply. Economical to use.

SHELL GARDEN SPRAYS

SHELL CHEMICALS LIMITED
(DISTRIBUTORS)

Norman House, 105-109 Strand London, W.C.2

MADE OF SWORDSTEEL · BY A SWORDSMITH
Tom Beasley

PERFECTION IN PRUNING!

Wilkinson Sword Pruning Shears are forged from the finest Swordsteel by craftsmen—that is why they are always the first choice of the expert. He knows their superb qualities.

W.42. POCKET PRUNER

Fitted with concealed spring and new sliding clip, it is the perfect instrument for light pruning, disbinding, etc. Light and compact, with RUST-RESISTING blades. Especially suitable for ladies.

Price 10/-

W.32. ROSE PRUNER

Designed for Rose Pruning, this model is also excellent for general pruning. The blades will ensure a clean cut, thus preventing unnecessary damage. **Price 17/6**

W. 32. ROSE PRUNER

Available from all stockists.
Write for descriptive leaflet G 15 of full range of Pruning Shears (10/- to 22/6) and Garden Shears (25/- to 45/-).

WILKINSON SWORD
PRUNING SHEARS

THE WILKINSON SWORD CO., LTD., Acton, London, W.4.
Makers of the famous Wilkinson Razor.